The Life and Ti

THE MATRONS
OF THE
NEWCASTLE INFIRMARY

1751 – 1976

NEWCASTLE INFIRMARY 1751 - 1887
ROYAL INFIRMARY 1887 - 1906
ROYAL VICTORIA INFIRMARY 1906 - 1976

Anne Craft

This book commemorates

"The beneficence and devotion of those Matrons who served the old Infirmary on the Forth Banks and the Royal Victoria Infirmary for a period of two hundred and twenty five years"

Non Nobis Solum
Not for ourselves alone
1751-1976

(A paraphrase of the words on the tablet placed in the entrance hall to the RVI in 1951)

Published by:
City of Newcastle Upon Tyne
Newcastle Libraries
Tyne Bridge Publishing, 2019
www.tynebridgepublishing.org.uk

CONTENTS

Foreword
Preface
Introduction

FOREWORD

Care giver, economist, workforce analyst, trainer, educator, infection control specialist, leader, manager, nurse; the developing role of the Matron was a crucial step in the creation of a modern, progressive hospital system, a key stage in the transition of the nurse from domestic servant to health care leader.

'Matrons of the Newcastle Infirmary 1751-1976' is a piece of historical research that illuminates the worlds of the women who held the position of Matron in Newcastle across the centuries. It is an enthralling exploration of their lives, their roles and their influence on the hospital, the patients and the nursing profession.

The brave and courageous women who undertook the role of Matron at the Infirmary, Newcastle upon Tyne, developed skills and confidence as leaders through difficult and challenging periods in the history of healthcare. At their inception hospital nursing was seen as an extension of domestic service and nurses had a public image of ignorance and slovenly or even drunken behaviour; the Infirmary sought to appoint women of distinction and challenge this negative stereotype.

These Matrons shaped and developed their role against a background of industrial revolution, political upheaval, world war and the struggle for the emancipation of women. They produced firm rules and regulations for both patients and staff, and through the decades as their skills and competencies developed they ensured patients received adequate care against a background of problematic social conditions. Whilst the appointment of Matron addressed the need to improve hospital hygiene and cleanliness, their legacy reaches well beyond this.

The Matron was crucial to the effective management of infection control. She was responsible for nurse training activity, nursing on the wards and for ensuring every aspect of cleanliness in the wards, clinics and operating theatres. The pursuit of this goal lead to the development of nurse education and academia and the addition of a scientific basis to the training of nurses. The broad and diverse backgrounds from which Matrons were appointed at the Infirmary brought distinctive qualities to the role and allowed the refinement and expansion of their function and responsibilities. This diversity empowered the Matrons to overcome the challenges they faced in their line of duty.

The historical and modern role of the Matron remains a powerful force in healthcare. Modern nursing has better working conditions, greater flexibility, degree level education, improved scope of practice and improved professional regulation when compared to the trailblazers whose lives we witness here, however their legacy can be felt every step of the way.

The restructure of hospital staff following the publication of the Salmon Report in 1966 and the centralisation of many NHS services saw the diminishing role of the nursing figurehead - only to re-emerge as a 'Modern Matron' in the early 21st Century to tackle the MRSA dilemma. These women, and now men as well, have seen their role and responsibilities change considerably. In Newcastle, the Infirmary Matrons have emerged as strong, firm and fair nurses who have formed and shaped important contributions to the health service alongside their clinician colleagues. The role of the Matron in policy initiatives, professional regulation, performance and organisational change can be seen threaded throughout our history right up to today.

Nurse Leaders have always been at the forefront of change in healthcare - no other healthcare profession has such a broad and far-reaching role. The presence, skills, observation and vigilance of well educated and well led nurses provide a constant safe environment for patients and staff alike.

I have no doubt that the recognition of The Newcastle upon Tyne Hospitals NHS Foundation Trust as an 'Outstanding' organisation by the Care Quality Commission in 2019, for the second time, stems from the dedication, hard work and commitment of all its staff. The excellence of the nursing staff, under the leadership of Matrons across the centuries has brought the Trust to where it is today, a highly competent, caring and compassionate community who excel at putting the patient at the heart of healthcare.

As a nurse, midwife and educationalist who first trained at Newcastle General Hospital as a Cadet Nurse and recently returned to Newcastle Hospitals as a Non-Executive Director, I am completely assured as I revisit many of these women's life stories that the fundamental values of nursing have been embedded and their dedication and commitment continue to enhance both today's nurses and the future of the Newcastle Hospitals.

Professor Kathleen McCourt CBE FRCN RGN RM
May 2019

PREFACE

This history has been prepared as part of the celebrations for the 60th Anniversary of the Royal Victoria Infirmary Nurses' League in 2019. It is primarily a record for members, the majority of whom undertook their nurse training at the RVI during the decades leading up to 1976 when the RVI Nurse Training School merged with other Training Schools from across Newcastle to become the Newcastle upon Tyne School of Nursing located on the site of the Freeman Hospital. Nurse Education subsequently transferred into the University of Northumbria. It should also be of interest to a wider community interested in social history and the development of health care as well as those concerned with local history.

The RVI Nurses' League is by no means the oldest Nurses' League in the UK, many having been established much earlier; however it has survived with an active membership and well attended Annual Meetings. Not long after the founding of the League in 1959, by the then Matron Freda Shaw, the National Health Service became the subject of considerable change, which impacted on the organisation of nursing and the role of the hospital Matron in particular, and therefore this book will focus primarily on the Matrons between the 1750s and the 1970s, after which time, and in line with national policy, there were various mergers of the hospitals and schools of nursing in Newcastle with consequent changes in the management of nurses and nursing.

The history of the Newcastle Infirmary, later the Royal Infirmary, and subsequently the Royal Victoria Infirmary has already been documented, however whilst much has been recorded about the physicians and surgeons who have served the Infirmary since its inception, there is little on record about nursing, and in particular the Matrons, who have been an important cornerstone of the service provided for patients since 1751.

The Infirmary in 1855 facing south showing the addition of the Dobson Wing

Whilst there is always more research still to do, all of the individual Matrons have been identified, and some detail as to who they were is provided with reference to some of the local and national contextual issues of the times. For some of the individuals concerned it goes little beyond giving them a name, however that is more than many of us have had before! There is much to tell, including: the important role of the newspapers of the day; the advocacy of Infirmary surgeons Heath and Gibb in advancing the cause of nursing leadership and training; links between a Matron and Eno Fruit Salts; a Matron who contracted diphtheria in the line of duty, and was saved thanks to speedy intervention by the medical staff; another who tragically committed suicide and two who had trained during the 1860s & 1870s under the legendary Mrs Wardroper, Superintendent of the Nightingale School. In addition there are Matrons who had nursed in far-flung places before taking up post in the Infirmary, one whose father was a surgeon on a troop ship returning from Scutari with almost 200 injured soldiers, and later there were others who, in addition to their role in the Infirmary, took on additional responsibilities in the Territorial Force Nursing Service founded in 1908.

As well as providing some background to the individual post holders, this record also illustrates that as medical and surgical interventions became more complex, the role of Matron diversified and evolved from that which was essentially a Head of Housekeeping to that of Head of Nursing. The increasing demands resulted in the spawning en-route of the development of more specific/specialist roles, deputies and assistants, home sisters, nurse tutors and the gradual relinquishing of the housekeeping aspects of the work to other members of the ever-increasing range of hospital workers. The 1970s brought, amongst other things, the introduction of career managers and personnel departments, since when the speed of change has continued to escalate to this day as titles are subject to frequent change, new roles are constantly developing and structures once again reorganised. The hope is that patients and their needs remain the central focus of nurses and the Infirmary.

The Royal Victoria Infirmary

INTRODUCTION

In the mid-eighteenth century the population of Newcastle was about 23,000 but beginning to grow rapidly as the River Tyne was continuing to expand as a major trading centre, not least as a consequence of the local coal industry. Alongside this industrial and commercial development, philanthropic activity across the country was increasingly in evidence and much was directed towards the building and maintenance of hospitals for the sick poor. At this time hospitals were used only by those who were unable to pay for medical assistance; those who could afford to pay were expected to be treated at home.

Prior to the founding of the Newcastle Infirmary in 1751 there were already fourteen voluntary Infirmaries in England (Appendix 1). Five of these were in London and were in addition to St Bartholomew's and St Thomas' Hospitals both of which were originally religious establishments founded in the twelfth century, but re-founded as non-religious institutions following the dissolution of the monasteries.

In January 1751 a certain "B K" generally considered to be the eminent surgeon Mr Richard Lambert, wrote to the Newcastle Courant, bringing to public attention the need for an Infirmary for the relief of the sick and lame poor. The following week he submitted for the reader's information a detailed estimate of the annual expenses of such a hospital. He reported that he had carefully examined and compared the annual accounts of several of the hospitals in London and he was very certain that his calculation of £530 per annum would be found to be too high rather than too low. The response to this appeal was immediate and fulsome.

On the 23 March 1751 the newspaper reported that a house had been rented and listed the materials required to equip it for the reception of patients. It was also reported that Statutes, Rules and Orders for the Governance of the Infirmary had been agreed and printed.

The 13 April was designated as the day on which the physicians, surgeons, and servants of the Charity would be chosen. It was stipulated that candidates for the posts of Matron, House Steward or Secretary, upper and under Nurses, Cook and Porter must be supported by at least two of the Governors of the Charity.

Thus, pending the building of an Infirmary, on 23 May 1751, a house in Gallowgate was opened for the reception of both in-patients and out-patients. It could accommodate 23 patients and 7 were admitted on that first day. Within a short period of time more beds were made available by hiring rooms in neighbouring houses, providing accommodation for up to 40 patients.

By September 1751 the foundation stone of the new Infirmary on the Forth Banks was laid and it was ready for the reception of patients on 8 October 1753 at a cost of £3,697. It was designed by local architect William Newton, who subsequently went on to design the Newcastle Assembly Rooms.

The Infirmary stood in gardens and fields outside the city walls at the southeast corner of the site of the present Centre for Life, and was not demolished until the 1950s. It provided accommodation for 90 in-patients and whilst there was separate accommodation for men and women there was no discrimination between medical and surgical cases. The building formed two sides of a quadrangle, having a south and east front. The south wing, or main building, consisted of three stories and a basement, the east wing two stories. The ground floor of the main building comprised a board room, chapel, physician's room, surgery and Matron's parlour, whilst the floor above comprised three wards for men, i.e.: Durham, Newcastle and Northumberland as well as a "back" ward called Sydenham. The operating theatre was in the attic along with another two "back" wards named Cheselden and Harvey. The ground floor of the east wing contained two male wards, Job and B. K., the

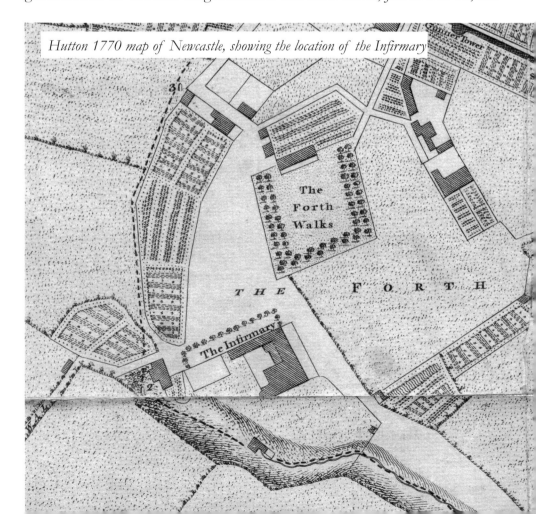

Hutton 1770 map of Newcastle, showing the location of the Infirmary

latter in honour of the author of the letter to the Newcastle Courant in 1751. The first floor of the east wing comprised three wards for women, i.e. Butler, Magdalen and Lazarette. Behind the main buildings stood the bakery and brew house, and not too far away the burial ground.

The demands made on the limited accommodation offered by the Infirmary extended far beyond its capacity. Pressure on the hospital beds became a problem almost from the beginning with reports of overcrowding and, on occasions, some patients having to share beds! There was, however, to be no increase in accommodation until the next century. Experience also showed that hospital admission was not suitable for many people; patients with any "infectious distemper" were dangerous to others and the dangers of admission were too great for young children and pregnant women.

Initially donations towards the upkeep of the Infirmary were generous but towards the end of the 18th century financial pressures increased. The national economy came under increasing pressure as a result of the war with France, and locally there were increasing demands on the Infirmary arising from the expanding population as well as improvements in medical treatments.

Arrangements for the Governance and Management of the Infirmary

The Governors of the Infirmary comprised the major benefactors, i.e. those who made a donation of at least £20, or those subscribers who made an annual donation of at least two guineas (£2.2s) to the charity. Governorship entitled individuals to attend and vote at the Quarterly Courts where major matters of policy and finance were discussed as well as agreeing the appointment of the House Committee for the following Quarter.

The House Committee initially comprised 12 members each from Newcastle, Northumberland and Durham and was responsible for the detailed care and supervision of the Infirmary. This Committee met weekly on a Thursday when they received reports from the Matron, and initially the Apothecary, but later the Resident Medical Officer. Each week the previous week's House Visitors also reported to the Committee, the House Visitors being appointed on a weekly basis.

Staff appointments were by election at the Court of Governors with each Governor having a vote. Candidates, as will be seen later, were allowed to canvas for support.

There were two resident officials, the Matron and the House Apothecary, both of whom were provided with their own office and sleeping room. The Apothecary was responsible for drugs and the making up of prescriptions as ordered by the Honorary Physicians, however he was also concerned with the day to day care of the medical patients and the general overseeing of the hospital. Together he and the Matron were responsible for discipline and were not allowed to be away from the hospital at the same time without special permission. Mr Henry Gibson, the first Apothecary, was paid £30 annually and remained in post for 23 years. Also appointed at this time were a porter and a brewer, on salaries of £8.8s and £7 respectively.

At the time of the opening of the Infirmary in 1751, the honorary medical staff comprised four physicians[1] and two surgeons[2], the latter being increased to four seven years later. Whilst a Resident House Surgeon was appointed in 1805, the numbers of Honorary Staff were not increased again until assistant surgeons were appointed in 1869 and assistant physicians in 1897. In spite of their lack of payment, the honorary medical staff were also subject to the Infirmary's Rules.

The Statutes and Rules, covering every aspect of the governance and management of the Infirmary, were first published in 1751 and subsequently revised in 1801 and from time to time thereafter well into the 20th century. Those of particular interest to the development of nursing in the Infirmary relate specifically to the Matron, Nurses and other Servants, and Patients and eventually, in 1868, the Housekeeper. As these Rules developed over the years, the changes will be tracked so that the context within which each Matron was working can be understood.

No patient, other than accident cases, could be admitted to the Infirmary without a "letter of recommendation" provided by either a Governor or a subscriber; a system that was to continue until 1888. The "letters of recommendation" were issued to subscribers in accordance with the tariff of the time; for example one in-patient, or two out-patients for a subscription of one or two guineas. The letters were valid for two months, after which the patient could be discharged regardless of recovery unless another letter was obtained. However three beds were to be kept for emergencies, i.e. "fractures and other dreadful accidents in need of immediate relief". Such cases could be admitted by the Apothecary or Matron who would then inform the Physicians and Surgeons.

[1] Physicians would have served an apprenticeship and also have studied and taken a Doctorate in Medicine, at a University – at that time in England, Oxford or Cambridge, or in Scotland, Edinburgh or Glasgow. They practised internal medicine, treating symptoms and complaints by giving advice and prescribing medicines which were then made up by Apothecaries (apprenticeship training with registration) who charged for their dispensing services and drugs.

[2] Surgeons: few were Doctors of Medicine; the majority were members of Surgeons or Barber-Surgeons Guilds and were admitted after 5 years' apprenticeship with a practising surgeon. They looked after the outside of the body treating injuries, dislocations, fractures – for which amputation was the usual treatment as infection was almost certain to follow. They also operated on cysts, superficial tumours, stone in the bladder, opened abscesses, and treated ulcers and skin conditions. They were not allowed to prescribe internal medicines. Both Apothecaries and Surgeons commonly flouted the regulations and did "general practice" for the great mass of people.

DOROTHY JACKSON
Matron 1751-1764

The appointment of Mrs Dorothy Jackson, the widow of William Jackson, a "yeoman", as the first Matron was announced in the local press on 23 April 1751. The background of Mrs Jackson is not known for certain, however for over a hundred years the main criteria for the post of Matron appeared to be that she should be a person of some social standing, accustomed to managing a household and servants. Widows without family encumbrances were often the preferred candidates. At the outset the role of the Matron was essentially that of a Housekeeper rather than of a Head of Nursing and it would not be until 1868 that expectations shifted and pressure grew to recruit a Lady (trained) Superintendent of Nurses. Dorothy's salary was initially £10 per annum (in comparison to the Apothecary's salary of £30); however by 1752 this had been raised to £15.

The Rules indicate that the Matron was responsible for the Infirmary's domestic arrangements, equipment and food supplies as well as discipline. In regard to the latter, it seems that the standard of behaviour of both patients and staff was not always high, with disorderly, dirty, and drunken habits amongst the patients and more rarely similar offences on the part of servants.

The Newcastle Infirmary 1753

The 1751 Rules for the Matron

1.   That the Matron take care of all the household goods and furniture, according to the inventory given to her; and that she be ready to give an account thereof when required.

2.   That she weigh and measure all the provisions and necessaries that come into the House, and keep a daily account thereof, to be given in to the Committee every Thursday, and never suffer any of them to be carried out. That she oversee the patients and servants, take care that the wards, chambers, beds, cloaths, [i.e. cloths] linen, and all other things within the Infirmary be kept neat and clean; and that to these ends all the patients and servants, shall be submissive and obedient to her.

3.   That she keep a diet book, by which the number of patients on each diet may be known; and wherein proper entrances and goodness, weight, and distribution of the provisions shall be distinctly made.

4.   That she go into each ward every morning and evening, and cause the names of all the patients to be called over; and that she enter in the House Visitors Book, the names of the patients who are absent at such times from their respective wards without her leave, or who have in any other respect transgressed the Rules of the Infirmary.

5.   That she take care of the keys of the doors, and see that the outer gates be always locked at nine in the evening, and not opened before seven in the morning, from Michaelmas to Lady-day; locked at ten in the evening and not opened before six in the morning, from Lady-day to Michaelmas; unless ordered otherwise by the Committee, or in cases of great emergency for the services of the patients.

6.   That she see that all the nurses, servants and patients do their duty, and observe the Rules of the House and that in the case of misbehaviour, or neglect, she acquaint the Committee or House Visitors therewith.

7.   That she do not receive any patient into the Infirmary without an order of the Committee, except in cases of accidents.

Nurses were appointed at the Matron's discretion for £4 a year, but, contingent on a year's faithful service, they were eligible to receive a gratuity not exceeding £2. The nurses were non-resident and were reported to be illiterate. Nursing at that time, and for over a hundred years to come, was an occupation followed by women of little education or means. Two nurses, Latimer and Campbell, had been appointed in 1751 and one of them was dismissed for insobriety prior the move to the Forth Banks. Subsequently nurses were not mentioned in any Annual Report until 1865 when eleven were recorded as being in post.

The 1751 Rules for Nurses and Servants

1.   That all persons concerned as servants be free from the burden of children and the care of the family.

2.   That a pound of meat and 3 ounces of butter and cheese be allowed every day to each servant in the Infirmary, and that all the nurses shall dine together at a stated time with the other common servants.

3.   That a table of diet be hung in every ward for the information of the patients; and that the patients on Low Diet be served first at every meal.

4.   That no liquors or provisions of any sort be brought into the House to the patients from their friends or any others whatsoever.

5.   That the nurses clean their respective wards before seven in the mornings, from the first of March to the first of October, and before eight from the first of October to the first of March. And that they serve up all the breakfasts within an hour after the wards are cleaned.

6.   That the nurses and other servants be very diligent in complying with the orders of the Matron and their superior; and that they behave themselves with tenderness to all patients and with civility and respect to all.

7.   That no servant belonging to the Infirmary having been once removed for misbehaviour by a Quarterly Court of Governors, be capable of being taken again in the service of the House.

8.   That when any patient dies in the Infirmary the nurses shall immediately deliver up all their effects to the Matron (This was added into the 1752 edition of the Rules).

It is very difficult indeed to imagine the daily life in a ward during this time. Whilst men and women were nursed separately, there was no distinction between medical and surgical patients and for the most part the patients nursed each other. A very ill, or an obstreperous patient, would be put into a room along with a convalescent patient to control and care for him. Complaints from the patients regarding the food were not infrequent; and in 1754, following a complaint about the quality of the beer and meat the complainants were ordered to have only tea and toast for a week, although the amount of malt in the beer was increased! The patients, like everyone else, were expected to abide by the Infirmary's Rules which amongst others, stipulated that:

1. They were not to leave the Infirmary without prior permission;
2. They were expected to rise by 7am in the summer and 8am in the winter and be in bed by 10pm in the summer and 9pm in the winter;
3. Swearing, cursing, abusive language and indecent behaviour were forbidden and men and women were not allowed to visit each other's wards;
4. Patients discharged because of bad behaviour were not allowed readmission to the Infirmary unless they were an accident case;
5. The playing of cards, dice, or any other game and smoking were forbidden without the consent of the doctor;
6. Those patients fit enough to work were to assist in the nursing of the patients, the washing and ironing of linen, and the washing and cleaning of the wards, as well as "doing such other business as the Matron shall require";
7. No reward was to be taken by any officer or servant from the patients or their friends either before or after admission;
8. In-patient status was limited to a period of no more than eight months.

The Infirmary

In early June 1751 soon after the opening of the House in Gallowgate there was a notice in the local press indicating that old linen for dressings and bandages would be accepted by the Infirmary. Such notices would appear from time to time over the next one hundred and fifty years with regular letters in the local press from the "Matron" expressing gratitude for the gifts of old linen. However by 1874 it was evident that the Infirmary was providing a collection service for such contributions!

NEWCASTLE INFIRMARY.
THE Committee will be exceedingly obliged for Presents of OLD LINEN or CALICO. If word is left at the Infirmary, messengers will be sent for the same. [3109

At the time of the transfer of services into the Infirmary on the Forth Banks in October 1753, Dorothy was reported as having been busy removing the patients and goods from the Gallowgate House for ten days prior to the transfer of services from the house in Westgate to the new premises.

	1751-52	1752-3
Wages for "servants, and extraordinary nursing and watchers"	£72.15.5d.	£100.19.6d.
Total Expenditure	£943.2.11d (Aprox £350 of this was expended on "fitting up the house")	£606.15.5 ¾d

Table 1. Summary of Infirmary running costs for the first two years

	1751-52		1752-1753	
	Admissions	Out-Patients	Admissions	Out-Patients
Amputation	15		12	
Asthma				15
"Complications"		13		
Consumption	10	13	12	23
Contusions		10		
Dropsical			18	15
Flux & Bloody Flux				11
Fractures			13	
Rheumatism, Sciatica etc.	11	11		13
Strains				10
Strumous & Scrophulous	16	24		22
Ulcers	17			
Wounds		10		14
Other reasons	98	97	90	95
Total Admissions/Attendances	**167**	**178**	**145**	**218**
Deaths	11		12	

Table 2. Summary of the most common reasons for admission/attendance to the Infirmary, 1751-1753

The first two Annual Reports have been reviewed and detail is summarised in Tables 1 & 2 providing insights into the early days of the Infirmary, both in regard to the type of patients admitted and the costs incurred in the provision of the service. It is of interest to compare the first table with the projected expenditure of £530 provided by "B K" in January 1751.

Amputation would only have been performed as a last and desperate resort. General anaesthetic was not yet available and the patients would be conscious and without pain relief. Such surgical intervention would have been beset with terror, agony as well as considerable risk for the patients; and of course the need for a surgeon with a strong nerve and attendants with tremendous strength of character! Although not included in table 2 "cutting for the (bladder) stone" was at this time another relatively common surgical procedure and there is a record of this being performed for the first time in the Infirmary on November 14th 1751, the stone in question weighing 2 ounces. The patient subsequently appeared before the House Committee to offer his gratitude. Such operations were obviously considered newsworthy as the following announcement appeared in the local press in July 1754:

> Laſt Week a Man aged 56 and a Boy four Years old, who had been cut for the Stone, were diſcharg'd cured, from the Infirmary. Theſe are the fifth and ſixth Patients who have been cured by that Method.

Income generation was obvious alive and well in 1754 with an interesting notice appearing in the local press:

> **INFIRMARY, NEWCASTLE,**
> JULY, 25, 1754.
>
> THE BATHS being now finiſhed, are ready for the Accommodation of the Publick, on the following Terms,
> COLD BATH,
> To Non-ſubſcribers, Six-pence each Time.
> To all Subſcribers of one Guinea per Ann. and upwards, Gratis.
> HOT BATH and BAGNIO,
> To Non-ſubſcribers, Half a Crown each Time.
> To Subſcribers of one Guinea per Ann. and upwards, one Shilling.
> CUPPING, Half a Crown.
> By Order of the Committee, R. BURDUS, Secretary.

Dorothy Jackson died in Newcastle in October 1764, her age unknown, and was buried at St Nicholas Church in Newcastle. Her now vacant post was advertised in the local press later that month. Candidates were requested to submit in writing to the Secretary of the Infirmary, for consideration by a Special Committee of Governors, details of their respective ages, characters, abilities and qualifications, along with an account of the manner in which they had lived, or the places in which they had served, people of credit whom they had attended or the masters or mistresses with whom they have served. The names of 10 candidates, all married, were published in the Newcastle Chronicle on 8 December 1764.

Further to this notice the following week the same newspaper published, for the information of prospective candidates, the Rules to be observed by the Matron and noted that the salary of the Matron would be £15 per annum with diet, washing and lodgings. It was also noted that the late Matron, some years after entering her office, had an annual gratuity of five guineas, as an acknowledgement and reward of good faithful service.

Timeline

1756 The Bank of Newcastle opened in Pilgrim Street – the country's first provincial bank outside of London and Edinburgh to rely solely on the business of banking.

1760 King George III ascended to the throne on the death of King George II.

1760 The Lying-in Hospital was opened in Rosemary Lane in Newcastle for "poor, married woman or widows pregnant at the time of their husband's deaths".

1763 The Newcastle Lamp and Watch Act was passed. This stated that up to 50 able-bodied men would be paid to "watch within the wall" between 29 September and 25 March and whenever else required. Their job was to "prevent all mischiefs happening by fires, as all murders, burglaries, robberies and other outrages and disorders". They had the power to arrest nightwalkers, malefactors and suspected persons who were found wandering and misbehaving themselves. The service was paid for by a special levy on land rent. The Act also provided for the provision of lighting the town with oil lamps. The areas beyond the city walls were not included until 1812.

MARGARET JACKSON
Matron 1765-1798

At the General Quarterly Court held at the Infirmary on 3 January 1765, Mrs Margaret Jackson of Stella, situated on the south side of the Tyne near Ryton, was elected Matron of the Infirmary. She would have been about 57 years old. Her appointment, subsequently reported in the Newcastle Courant, noted that Margaret was the widow of Robert Jackson, a "*Staithman of Stella*"[1]. During the 1730s the Jackson family also provided facilities for steeple-chasing on their land at Stella. Records indicate that a Robert Jackson of Stella had died in 1741 and was interred at Holy Cross Church in Ryton, and it is assumed that this was Margaret's husband. Soon after Margaret's appointment this letter appeared in the local press:

To *the* GOVERNORS *of the* INFIRMARY,

GENTLEMEN,

PErmit me to return you my most humble and hearty Thanks for the Honour you have done me, in electing me to be MATRON of the INFIRMARY; and be assured that I will execute that Trust with the utmost Diligence, Fidelity and Care; and am,

GENTLEMEN,

Newcastle,   Your obedient Servant,

Jan. 4, 1765.   MARGARET JACKSON.

Some insights into the work of the Infirmary during the years of Margaret's tenure can be drawn from the 1774 Annual Report which, whilst giving no detail regarding the conditions of the patients accepted for treatment, does record what amounted to be at least a four-fold increase in the number of patients treated since the early 1750's with 679 in-patients and 678 out-patients. It was also noted that 135 accident cases had been admitted and that there had been 23 in-patient deaths. Expenditure had risen to £1776.12.10d of which a modest £167.8.4½d was in respect of "*wages, gratuities and extraordinary nurses and watchers*".

In his PhD Thesis of 2012 "*Disease, Medicine & the Urban Poor in Newcastle upon Tyne 1750-1850*", Graham A Butler tabulated the reasons for admission to the Infirmary as well as the length of stay of in-patients for the period 1778-1787 and this gives some further insight into the work undertaken by the Infirmary during this period. These have been summarised in Table 3 and shows that accidents accounted for over a quarter of the Infirmary's admissions; such patients would of course have been received without the mandatory letter from a subscriber or governor.

Both In-Patients & Out-patients	Number Treated	% of Patients
Wounds, Injuries & Fractures	1108	26.00%
Rheumatism	706	16.80%
Ague (fever)	540	12.80%
Scurvy	268	6.40%
Asthma	170	4.00%
Stone	167	4.00%
Hernia	137	3.30%
Hectic (fever linked to consumption)	107	2.50%
Fits	51	1.20%
Diarrhoea	50	1.20%
Dysentery	50	1.20%
Epilepsy	48	1.10%
Dropsy	45	1.10%
Gout	45	1.10%
Pox	44	1.00%
Indigestion	43	1.00%
Others less than 1%	626	14.80%
Total	**4205**	**100%**

Table 3. Reasons for admission, 1778-1787

The length of stay data in Table 4 is interesting in light of the aforementioned Rules for Patients which stated that "no patient continue in the hospital for more than eight months" which depending upon how it was calculated, would have amounted to between 224 to 243 days.

Length of stay in days	Total number of in-patients	Percentage of patients
1-40	301	15.4%
41-80	374	19.2%
81-120	246	12.6%
121-160	290	14.9%
161-200	249	12.8%
201-240	227	11.6%
241-280	162	8.3%
280	100	5.1%
Total	**1949**	**100%**

Table 4. Lenght of stay of in-patients, 1778-1787

Other than what can be gleaned from the admission records there is a dearth of information regarding Margaret Jackson's 33 years in post, although it was recorded that on 19 October 1797, the Matron informed the Committee that it was customary to illuminate the House upon particular occasions. She was consequently ordered to "illuminate the House this night" on account of the glorious victory obtained by Admiral Duncan over the Dutch fleet off Camperdown, north of Haarlem on 11 October and with this success the threat of a French invasion[2] faded.

As a consequence of the rising prices and taxes arising from the war, financial pressures began to impact on the charity's income, and there is evidence that the Infirmary had been forced to restrict the allowance of bread to patients. Newcastle meanwhile was benefitting from the war effort with, amongst others, the armaments, foundries and iron industries flourishing, although it seems that the poor received a scanty share of the prosperity as wages were kept down by the rapid increase in the population.

Little is known about the nursing staff of the Infirmary during this period, however in June 1791 an advert appeared in the local press for "A nurse wanted at Lammas[3] next for the Women's Ward – enquire of the Matron".

Margaret died in post on 9 December 1798 at the age 90 and she was buried in the parish of Ryton. Four days later a letter from her daughter Mary Jackson

Holy Cross, Ryton c1890

l in the Newcastle Courant letter; she was seeking support to succeed
ıer as Matron of the Infirmary. Mary reported that for the last twelve
: had assisted her mother in her capacity as Matron and she hoped
that this would therefore operate as a motive for the Governors to favour her
application. It seems that it was not uncommon at this time, and for some
years afterwards, for candidates applying for a senior post in the Infirmary to
publish such letters before the scheduled meeting of the Governors.

Timeline

1766 A privately run asylum for those who could afford to pay, was opened in Spital Tongues. Initially known as St. Luke's its subsequently became known as the Bellgrove Retreat. A year later the Lunatic Asylum for the poor was opened in Warden's Close. Both of these institutions closed in the 1850s.

1777 The Dispensary was opened, initially in The Side, to give advice and medicine to the poor sick unable to access the Infirmary. It was one of the first centres to provide inoculation against smallpox. Dr John Clark founded the Dispensary and in 1788 he was appointed honorary physician to the Infirmary.

1796 After 1796 vaccination from cowpox, established by Edward Jenner, became almost universal. The transference of the infective agent from a smallpox patient to a healthy individual as a means of prevention had been advocated since about 1747 and from 1777 the physicians of the Dispensary in Newcastle had been using direct human inoculation, persuading more and more of the population to take up this preventive measure.

[1] Staiths were timber or stone-built loading platforms or jetties built on the shore of a river with relatively deep water alongside to allow the mooring and loading of ships or boats. A staithman was a person of some significance in the coal trade who managed the use of the coal staiths and controlled the loading of coal and unloading of ballast.

[2] To counter the threat of aggression from the newly created Dutch Republic during the war against France, a North Sea fleet of the Royal Navy had been formed with Duncan at its command. War with France had broken out in 1793 as the French Revolutionaries declared war on all the monarchies of Europe.

[3] Lammas was a quarter-day/holiday in August celebrating the annual grain harvest

MARY JACKSON
Assistant Matron 1786-1798
Matron 1799-1816

On 5 January 1799 the following letter appeared in the Newcastle Courant:

To the Presidents, Vice-Presidents, and Governors of the Infirmary, at Newcastle

Ladies and Gentlemen,

The zealous exertion of your services in my favour having happily secured to me the situation of Matron in this House, for which I so earnestly solicited your votes and interest, permit me now to request your acceptance of my most grateful thanks for the honour you have done me, and to assure you, that the great object of my sincere endeavours shall be to convince all who are interested in the prosperity of the Infirmary, that your confidence has not been misplaced, and that my conduct in office, in which your kindness has placed me, shall correspond with the professions which I made to obtain it.

I have the honour to be, with the most dutiful respect,

Ladies and Gentlemen,

Your most obliged and devoted humble servant,

Mary Jackson.
Infirmary, Jan. 3rd, 1799

Alongside Mary Jackson's letter, there was another from a Mrs Smiles who offered her thanks to those Governors of the Infirmary who had honoured her with their patronage and support in the election of a Matron.

Thus the first three Matrons of the Infirmary all shared the surname Jackson, and two were mother and daughter!

During the early years of Mary Jackson's tenure the attendance of House Committee members had declined to such an extent that the governance of the Infirmary had fallen more and more into the hands of the Matron and Apothecary, with the minute book recording that in their absence the Matron had undertaken this or that responsibility. For example, in 1800 Mary Jackson ed the following entry in the House Visitors book:

n-attendance of the Committee (I) have been under the necessity of taking upon myself to apply to another Baker instead of Mr Harrison who has of late supplied the House with bread very unsuitable both in respect of quantity and quality."

Such incidents reinforced a growing awareness, thanks in no small part as a result of the efforts of Dr John Clark, an honorary physician at the Infirmary since 1787, of a need to review and update the Statutes and Rules that governed the Infirmary. As one consequence of the 1801 update, the number of members of the House Committee was reduced to 12 ordinary, who lived locally, and 36 extraordinary members having the option to attend. Another addition to the Rules related to the professional conduct to be observed by the physicians and surgeons who were instructed that *"the feelings and emotions of the patients, under critical circumstances, require to be known and attended to, no less than the symptoms of their diseases."*

Meanwhile existing Rules for the Matron were strengthened whilst some entirely new ones appeared, i.e.:

1. That she shall treat the patients with good nature and civility, and never suffer any degree of insolence or neglect from the servants, toward them, to pass unnoticed.

2. That she shall not employ any patient in the work of the house, without first obtaining leave from his or her physician or surgeon.

3. That when the weather is fine, she shall order a certain number of the mattresses, sheets, blankets, and quilts, of every bed in the wards, in rotation, to be hung over a line in the court yard, till they be well aired; that such a quantity of the bedding in use shall be exposed in succession, as that the whole may be purified in the space of fourteen days; and that this necessary work may be done without confusion, and with expedition, the following regulations shall be observed:-
a. That the mattress, sheets, blankets, and quilt of each bed shall have numerical mark, corresponding with that of the bed to which they belong;
b. That such patients as have permission from their physician or surgeon, shall assist in carrying down and bringing back the bedding;
c. That the nurses shall superintend and direct this business.

4. That she shall take care that all patients who are able, do regularly attend divine service in the chapel, and that she shall appoint a proper person in each ward publicly to read over, every Sunday morning, the rules which relate to the patients and nurses.

Fifty years after opening its doors the Infirmary was still reliant on patie
assisting with the work of the institution. This was understandable given the
very small numbers of nurses; only nine, even 40 years later. More specific
regulations were also established in respect of the care and cleanliness of bed
linen and mattresses. The Matron's role in policing chapel attendances as well
as ensuring that both patients and nurses were aware of the "*House Rules*" was
also made explicit. It was stipulated that the 1801 Rules for Nurses and Other
Servants were to be framed and hung up in every ward, and that "*Such Nurses
as do not strictly obey these rules shall be discharged from the service of the House*". These
Rules are transcribed overleaf.

The Rules for the Patients were also updated at this time and along with the
"Tables of Diet" provide further insights into the life inside the Infirmary
early in the nineteenth century. By this time the chewing of tobacco had been
added to the list of things which patients were not allowed to do. Patients
were also expected to wash their face and hands each morning and those who
were unable to use a bath were required to have their feet washed every
Thursday evening. If a patient's condition deteriorated overnight he/she had
to ask another patient to call for one of the nurses who would then inform
the house surgeon or apothecary.

Those who were well enough were expected to help the nurses and other
servants "in nursing the other patients, washing and ironing the linen, and in
doing such other business as the matron shall direct". The 'Tables of Diet',
identified Common, Reduced, and Milk Diets, with details provided for
breakfast, dinner and supper for each day Sunday through to Saturday.
Guidance was also given for a Low Diet, for those "in a state of fever, and
after accidents and operations of consequence". An example of the Common
Diet in 1801 is given in Table 5 below:

Breakfast:	A pint to a pint and a half of milk pottage, or a pint of hasty pudding with milk*
Dinner:	A pint of broth, with 8oz of boiled mutton, beef, or veal, and vegetables
Supper:	A pint of broth and vegetables

**According to Mrs Beaton the ingredients of Hasty Pudding were
milk, sugar, flour, salt and tapioca or sago*

In addition there was also a daily allowance of a pint and a half of beer and
a loaf of bread, weighing 12oz. In regard to the broth, every gallon included
either three pounds of mutton or veal, or two pounds of lean beef, over and
above the common allowance of meat.

...... .he Nurses, and other servants, shall obey the House-Surgeon and Apothecary, and the Matron, as their master and mistress; that they shall behave with civility and respect to strangers, and that they shall withdraw whenever the House-Visitors enter the wards.

2. That the Nurses shall punctually obey the orders of the Physicians and Surgeons, and behave with tenderness to all the patients; and if any patient shall not observe the rules hung up in the wards, or otherwise misbehave, the nurse shall complain immediately to the House-Surgeon and Apothecary, or the Matron, and if the complaint be not properly attended to by them, she shall inform the House-Visitors, or the House-Committee.

3. That the Nurses shall punctually administer medicines prescribed by the Physicians and Surgeons, according to the directions given by the House-Surgeon and Apothecary; and that they shall be particularly attentive to carry back as soon as possible all empty phials, &c., into the shop.

4. That the Nurses shall be very attentive to the state and symptoms of the patients, in order that they may be able to report them distinctly to the Physicians, Surgeons, or House-Surgeon and Apothecary; and if any threatening symptoms come on, that they shall instantly give notice to the House-Surgeon and Apothecary, that the Physicians or Surgeons, under whose care the patients are, may be speedily appraised of it.

5. That the Nurses shall take care to prevent the patients who are sufficiently able to sit up, from lying down on their beds with their clothes on.

6. That the Nurses shall be particularly careful that none of the patients receive from their friends, or conceal about their beds, victuals or liquors of any kind; and, likewise, that no portion of the provisions, &c., belonging to the house, be conveyed out of the Infirmary; that upon the discovery of any patient being guilty of receiving improperly, giving, or carrying away victuals, liquors, they shall not neglect to acquaint the Matron; and that they shall not admit any stranger or other visitor into the wards, without leave of the House-Surgeon and Apothecary, or the Matron.

7. That any Nurse who shall connive at patients leaving their wards, or being absent from the Infirmary, without permission from their physicians or surgeons, or the House Surgeon and Apothecary, and shall not make a report to the House-Surgeon and Apothecary of such patients being missing, shall be discharged from the House.

8. That the Nurses shall clean their respective wards and rooms with soap and warm water, or ley, twice in every week, before eight o'clock in the morning, from the first of March to the first of October; and before nine o'clock in the morning, from the first of October to the first of March; and that they shall mop their respective ward once every week, on an intermediate day, before the same hours, and keep the wards clean swept in the mean time; and that no sand shall be used on any account.

9. That the Nurses shall scald the chamber-pots every morning, and scour them twice a week, and that they shall allow no chamber-pot to remain in the wards during the day, except in cases of necessity.

10. That the Nurses shall pay great attention to the beds and linen of the patients, and particularly observe the following directions:
a) Whenever a patient dies or is discharged, the bed and mattress shall be exposed to the open air, and where circumstances require it, the bed shall be new stuffed, and the blankets, bed-linen, and quilts shall be washed.
b) The sheets of patients remaining for a length of time in the house shall be changed once a fortnight, or oftener, if necessary; the rest of the bed clothes once in two months; and when the patients have sores, once a month.
c) The shirts of the patients shall be changed once in four days, and their nightcaps and stockings once a week, or oftener, if necessary.
d) No foul linen, or bed clothes, shall be suffered to remain in the wards, but shall be taken to the wash-house, and the Matron informed, that she may give orders for their being properly washed.

11. That in each ward, during the day, the Nurses shall keep one window open, or more, according as the changes of the season, and the state of the weather may permit, and agreeably to the direction of the Physicians, Surgeons, or the House Surgeon and Apothecary; and that they shall not suffer any dirt, rags, or tow to remain in the wards, nor any clothes to be hung out at the windows.

12. That when any patients die in the house, the Nurses shall immediately deliver up all their effects to the Matron.

Mary's tenure was a period of change in the Infirmary. During its first 50 years there had been no modification to the structure of the building and very little in the way of medical and surgical advances. However, the population in Newcastle had risen to 28,000 by 1801 and the pressures on beds was unrelenting, added to this it was now evident that the wards were too large, badly ventilated, and insanitary with the patients too closely crowded into them. The bedsteads were made of wood with vermin-friendly flock mattresses, and there was only one room available for isolating infected or seriously ill patients.

In addition the southerly aspect of some of the wards meant that the patients had little protection from strong sunlight. The aforementioned Dr John Clark circulated the Governors with a report describing the "Result of an inquiry into the state of various Infirmaries with a view to the improvement of the Infirmary at Newcastle". Clark noted that over the two previous years the mortality rate at the Infirmary was 1 in 16, with 9 out of 59 patients admitted with compound and simple fractures having died, whilst 5 of the 6 patients admitted with a fractured skull had died. He made numerous recommendations regarding improvements to ventilation in the Infirmary as well as the replacement of the wooden bedsteads with those made of iron.

The matter was taken up by the Governors and in 1801 work commenced on both extending the main building on the west side and also reconfiguring the use of some of the accommodation within the existing Infirmary. With the loss of one ward on the ground floor of the east wing provision was made for a medical library, museum, a consulting hall, a waiting room and a dispensary. In addition, in an effort to reduce infection, the remaining wards were divided to provide no more than seven beds in each.

The Infirmary with 1801 extention

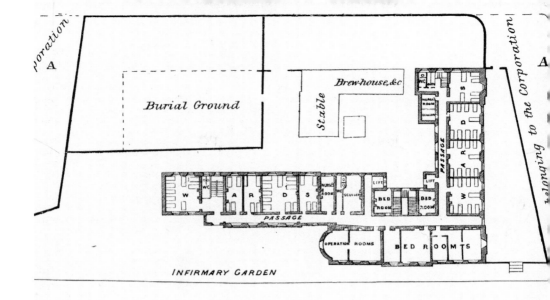

A plan showing the original Infirmary with additions, 1801-03

On completion of this reconstruction in 1803 the Infirmary increased the available beds by only 15 beds, but the opening the following year of the Fever Hospital[1], in Warden's Close just outside the town walls, would result in easing some of the bed pressures.

It is recorded that towards the end of 1804 the daily number of inpatients was between 100 & 112. Records suggest that by 1810 almost 1,000 patients had been treated during the year and about 200 surgical operations carried out. In 1805 the first Resident House Surgeon, Frederick Glenton, was appointed replacing the position of Resident Apothecary. For the next 65 years the Infirmary continued to function with only one Resident House Surgeon.

Mary Jackson resigned in 1816 and, at the age of 80 years, she died "at the Forth" in Newcastle in August 1817, and like her mother was buried at Holy Cross Church, Ryton. The announcement of her death in the local press reported that she had resided at the Infirmary for 30 years and had served diligently and faithfully the post of Matron for 18 years. Mary made bequests in her will to her two brothers Robert and Jacob, both of whom lived at Blunt's Wall Farm, Great Burstead, Essex; however Jacob had predeceased her by several months. Jacob had at least one child, another Mary, who died in unknown circumstances in Rome in 1863. Mary also bequeathed £10 to the Infirmary; currently equivalent to about £800.

The Fever Hospital, opened in 1804, and eased the pressure on the Infirmary

[1] The Fever Hospital, also known as the House of Recovery: patients were looked after by doctors from the Dispensary. Cath, one of the nurses of the Infirmary married Mr William Henderson, a pitman and one-time patient of the Infirmary, and when the Fever Hospital opened in 1804 she was appointed Matron, whilst her husband was appointed Inspector. They held these positions until her death in 1826. William Henderson at some point added 'doctor' to his name.

ELEANOR PATTISON
Matron 1816-1849

Notice of a Special Court of the Governors to be held in the Infirmary during October 1816 for the election of a Matron was announced in the local press, and that:

"Every candidate for the Office of Matron must be healthy, not above 40 years of age, free from the burden of a family, and must leave with the House-Committee, previous to the Day of Election, Testimonials of her Qualifications and Character"

The proposed salary for the post was forty guineas per annum. In the event the election was delayed until December, but meanwhile the following letter was published:

To the Governors of the Newcastle Infirmary , November 21st 1816

Ladies and Gentlemen,

Upon the resignation of Mrs Jackson, as matron of the infirmary, I take the liberty of offering, myself as a candidate for that situation, being hopeful that the testimonials I shall have to produce will give complete satisfaction, with respect to the requisites necessary to fulfil the duties of that important charge. Should I have the honour of being approved of by you, allow me to assure you that my exertions for the welfare of the institution shall be unremitting.
I have the honour to be, ladies and Gentlemen
Your humble servant,

Eleanor Pattison
Northumberland Street

Eleanor was subsequently appointed Matron, a position which she held for the next 32 years. She was born in 1780 and baptised on 21 May of that year in St Andrew's Church, Newcastle. Eleanor was the daughter of William and Eleanor Pattison of the Water Works, St Andrew's Parish in Newcastle; her Sister Ann was born in 1783. Their father, described in his daughters' baptismal records as a 'yeoman' died, aged 65 years, in 1817 followed by their mother, aged 64 years, in 1819.

Whilst there is no detailed information regarding the numbers of nurses and servants in post during these years the information in Table 6, extracted from the Annual Accounts for the year 1825-26, provides evidence that the workforce was none too great for a hospital with over 100 in-patient beds.

House Surgeon	£60:00
Secretary	£42:00
Chaplain	£20:00
Matron	£42:00
Sub-Total	£164:00
Nurses & Servants*	£128:14:06d
Total	£292:14:06d
*this would include the salaries of all other staff	

Table 6. Salaries & wages for the financial year, 1825-26

This annual expenditure of £293 should be considered within the context of the expenditure on food and drink of £1210 and an overall expenditure for the Infirmary of £2749. The Infirmary at this time was still served by a total of eight honorary physicians and surgeons, supported by a resident house-surgeon.

In 1830 a third floor was added to the east wing of the Infirmary to create another 30 beds, however 22 of these were for the female patients from the Lock Hospital,[1] which had closed its doors due to lack of funds. This new ward was called the Magdalen Ward and was reserved for female patients with venereal disease. These patients looked after themselves, kept the wards clean, padded splints and rolled bandages and were reported to be the best behaved patients in the Infirmary. However the provision of an additional 8 beds for the acute work of the Infirmary did not solve the problem of ever-increasing demands and in 1846 another 20 beds were added to the Infirmary's bed complement; but this simply increased the overcrowding of the wards.

Meanwhile Eleanor Pattison had the distinction of being in post at the time of the first UK population census on 6 June 1841, providing more details than were previously available about the staff of the Infirmary. The census provided the names, occupations and age of each person rounded down to the nearest 5 years, although the actual age was given for children under 15 years of age. On the day in question there were 125 patients in the Infirmary comprising: 78 males including two boys aged 3 and 9 years; and 47 females including two girls aged 2 and 5 years. Table 7 summarises the information provided about the 21 members of staff in the post.

It will be interesting to note how the age profile of the nursing staff gradually changed over the following decades, but at this time the emphasis was

The Infirmary in 1830

Position Held	No	Ages to nearest 5 years	Comments
House Surgeon:		25	Held this position from 1838 – 1846
Allen Joseph Taylor	1		
Matron:		55	Born in Northumberland, (which at that time would have included Newcastle).
Eleanor Pattison	1		
Dispenser:	1	20	
Medical Pupils:	2	20 & 15	
Nurses:	9	65, 60, 60, 50, 50, 45, 40, 40, & 35	
Porters:	2	Both 25	
Servants	5	45, 20, 20, 20, & 15	

Table 7 Staff in post, 1841

obviously on recruiting older females free from domestic responsibilities. Of the five servants the eldest was Eleanor's sister, Ann Pattison, and some years later in 1857 her death was announced in the Newcastle Courant:

"In Sandyford-lane, on 21st October, aged 72, much respected, Miss Ann Pattinson, for many years assistant matron of the Newcastle Infirmary."

Although there is a discrepancy in the spelling of the surname the other details match those on the family memorial. It was probably her retirement that prompted the appearance, in November 1844, of an advertisement in the local press requesting applications from unmarried women for the post of Superintendent Nurse at the Infirmary. This was evidently a new post, subordinate to the Matron and filled by Elizabeth Dowson. This development probably acknowledges the increasing workload of the Matron and a need to more closely supervise the work of the nurses.

The 1751 Rules for Nurses and Servants had stipulated some of the daily allowance of provisions for the staff, however by 1846 there is a more detailed record of what the nursing staff could expect on a daily basis. Beverages were obviously also allowed on the wards where they worked, with coffee grinders being provided in each flat. The 'flats' refer to the floors on which a group of wards were situated.

Monday:	Cold meat, rice pudding, potatoes or greens	
Tuesday:	Boiled mutton, potatoes or turnips	
Wednesday:	Roast mutton, Yorkshire pudding, potatoes or greens	
Thursday:	Boiled beef, currant pudding, potatoes	
Friday:	Fish, (when dear, meat), potatoes or greens	
Saturday:	Beef or mutton pie, potatoes	*Table 8*
Sunday:	Roast beef, Yorkshire pudding, potatoes or greens	*Nurses'*
For each nurse/week	2oz of tea, 2oz of coffee in the berry, 8oz of fresh butter and 8oz of sugar. NB: Fruit pies as usual; and, when in season, roast veal/two geese	*Diet, 1846*

Eleanor Pattison's tenure coincided with the introduction of greater regulation of the training required by prospective physicians and surgeons. In 1815 the Apothecaries Act had made the Licence of the London Society of Apothecaries (LSA) a requirement for general practice in England. Subsequently in 1824 the College of Surgeons in London, founded in 1800, received a Royal Charter and began to hold examinations for Membership (MRCS).

Examination for both institutions were held in London, however they both recognised certain provincial medical schools, including from 1834 that in Newcastle. The possession of the both the LSA and MRCS became the recognised qualifications for general medical practice.

The Newcastle upon Tyne School of Medicine and Surgery had been founded in 1832 in premises in Bell's Yard, Pilgrim Street. One of the first eight students enrolled was John Snow[2]. The first course of more formal lectures commenced in October 1834 by which time the number of students had risen to 25 and the School had relocated to the unused Barber Surgeon's Hall adjacent to the Holy Jesus Hospital. In the 1841 Census 'Medical Pupils' featured amongst the Infirmary staff.

Dr John Snow

Towards the end of the 1840s the scope of surgery was increasingly widened by the discovery of the anaesthetic substances ether and chloroform which could, with relative safety, produce unconsciousness and insensitivity to pain. Thereafter the scope and range of surgery was transformed, speed was now not the overriding requirement and the patients were spared pain and shock. However the surgical revolution would not take off fully until the 1870's with the introduction of Lister's techniques of antisepsis.

On 12 January 1847 the first operation under a general anaesthetic (ether) was performed in the Infirmary by Sir John Fife, just one month after it had been used for the first time in England at the University College Hospital in London. In November 1847 the first narcosis induced by chloroform was self-administered by the Edinburgh obstetrician James Young Simpson. Very soon after this, on 28 January 1848, the first ever fatality resulting from choroform anaesthesia occurred in the Infirmary.

Hannah Greener, a fifteen year old who had already experienced an ether anaesthetic, died within three minutes of being given chloroform, by Dr Robert Glover, for removal of a toe nail. Dr Glover, who was on the staff of the Newcastle School of Medicine, had been the first to describe the anaesthetic properties of chloroform on animals in 1842. Whilst the coroner blamed the chloroform, Dr James Young Simpson contended that the brandy given to try and revive her combined with inadequate oxygen was the cause, and that mouth-to-mouth resuscitation would have revived Hannah, however Dr John Snow argued that the handkerchief method of giving chloroform was imprecise and recommended an inhaler.

The 1830s & 1840s also heralded the age of the railway and this impacted on the Infirmary as railway lines were driven through adjacent land. In 1839 the Newcastle to Carlisle line opened with a temporary terminus at Forth, the Central Station was opened by Queen Victoria in 1850. The Infirmary built originally in a rural setting was now increasingly subjected to loss of land as well as noise and pollution.

The death of Eleanor Pattison was recorded in the Newcastle Courant in January 1849 with the following announcement:

"At the Infirmary on the 10th inst. in the 69th year of her age, much respected Mrs Eleanor Pattison Matron of that Institution the duties of which office she discharged during a period upwards of 32 years."

Eleanor bequeathed £20 to the Infirmary. There is a memorial to Eleanor, her sister and parents in the church yard of St Nicholas, Gosforth.

Timeline

1816   The stethoscope was invented by the French physician Rene Laennec, and by the 1820s it had become widely used in the diagnosis of various chest conditions.

1822   The Newcastle Infirmary for Diseases of the Eyes was founded and based initially in Brunswick Place before moving to larger premises in Prudoe Street 2 years later.

1831/2 There were serious outbreaks of cholera in Newcastle and the North East of England, with crowding of the Fever House which had opened in 1804. The population in Newcastle was now 53,000.

1832   There was an attempt in Newcastle to establish a police force modelled on that established in London three years previously. Since 1763 Newcastle had been served by "watchmen", however the public were reluctant to have their individual freedoms crushed by a "military-style force" for which they had to pay! Resistance was not sustained and three years later twenty men, all aged between 25 and 45 years of age were appointed. They were required to be of good character, able to read, write and paid £4 pounds toward the cost of their uniform.

---

[1]Lock Hospital had been opened in a hired house in November 1814 within the City Walls near the Pink Tower and subsequently to Raff-yard Queen Street on the west side of the Castle for the care of women with venereal disease.
[2]John Snow, Physician, gained fame both as an epidemiologist and as a pioneer in the field of anaesthetics. In 1854, when he identified the Broad Street water pump as the source of the outbreak, he proved his theory that the disease was not airborne, but resulted from the ingestion of infected matter. In 1853 he administered chloroform to Queen Victoria during the birth of her eighth child Prince Leopold, and subsequently for the birth of her ninth child Princess Beatrice in 1857

ELIZABETH DOWSON
Superintendent Nurse 1844-1849
Matron 1849-1855

Elizabeth Dowson was the daughter of Lancelot Barron, a farmer. She was born in Hexham in about 1818 according to the 1851 census. Elizabeth Barron married William Dowson a draper, in Tuthill-stairs Baptist Chapel, Newcastle in February 1839. Both Elizabeth and William were living in The Close in Newcastle at the time of their marriage. William, aged 21 years, died from smallpox in 'The Forth' in July of that same year. The following letter of application for the post of Matron at the Infirmary appeared in the local press soon after Eleanor Pattison's death:

To the Governors of the Newcastle Infirmary
My Lords, Ladies, and Gentlemen,

A vacancy having occurred in the office of matron to your valuable institution, in consequence of the lamented death of Mrs Pattison, I beg respectfully to offer myself as a Candidate for that Office. Having been for some years Matron of the Gateshead Institution for Training Female Servants, and for the last four years filled the very responsible situation of Superintendent Nurse in the Infirmary, I trust the testimonials I shall be enable to submit to you will warrant me to soliciting your confidence and support.

I beg also to add, that I am at present fulfilling the Duties of Matron until a successor to Mrs Pattison is elected, and I can only assure you that, would you be pleased to elect me to that office my best exertions shall be used to fulfil the trusts confided to my care.

I have the honour to be,
My Lords, Ladies, and Gentlemen,
Your most obedient and humble servant

Elizabeth Dowson
Infirmary, January 18, 1849

Subsequently it was announced that the Special Court of the Infirmary Governors, in the absence of any other candidates, had elected Mrs Elizabeth Dowson to the post of Matron.

The 1851 census confirmed Elizabeth as a widow aged 33 years, and identified 171 in-patients along with the wife of one patient and the mother of another. There were now 26 members of staff, up 5 from the previous census, however there were still just 9 nurses in spite of there being almost 50 more patients than in 1841. The ages of the nurses ranged from 30 to 75 years. The Infirmary's dispenser at the time was recorded as James Crossley Eno, aged 23 years who subsequently became famous for his Fruit Salts.

Elizabeth would have much to contend with during her term of office, not least the upheaval in the hospital during major construction works. The inadequacies of the Infirmary were increasingly obvious with overcrowding of the wards and infection a constant concern. Moreover the local population had tripled over the previous hundred years as industry flourished. In 1851 the senior surgeon Dr Greenhow, house-surgeon Dr Gibb, along with the architect John Dobson visited hospitals in London and the provinces[1] to gain insight into modern hospital design. Subsequently Dobson submitted plans for a new wing, which were agreed and in 1852 the foundation stone of the "Dobson Wing" was laid. The new wing consisted of a basement, which housed the out-patient department and three storeys each containing two 24-bedded wards, giving a total of 144 beds. These new wards were named:

Lower Flat:	Victoria Ward & Percy Ward
Middle Flat:	Bishop Ward & Newcastle Ward
High Flat:	Northumberland Ward & Durham Ward

This development allowed a major rearrangement of the east wing of the hospital, although the Magdalen Ward remained on the third floor, the second floor now provided accommodation for the resident staff whilst the first floor was converted to provide a dining room, museum, library and large accident room.

Although the building was not opened until March 1854, with the Official Opening in January 1855, some patients had been housed there in the spring of 1853 during an outbreak of erysipelas and an epidemic of typhus, the latter having resulted in the death of an old and valued nurse. In August of that same year Newcastle was hit by a cholera epidemic, with 1,500 people dying over a period of nine weeks. Once again the unfinished wards of the Dobson Wing were brought into service and the reputation of the Infirmary was much enhanced in the eyes of the public as it opened its doors to the poor at all hours. The Annual Report for 1854 reported on the measures that had been taken in the Infirmary during this outbreak:

"...the most laudable efforts were made by the Matron, Nurses and Servants to keep every part clean and sweet .... chlorine of lime was sprinkled on the floors .... the tone of body strengthened as far as possible by increased allowance of diet"

A plan of the Infirmary with the addition of the Dobson Wing 1851-53

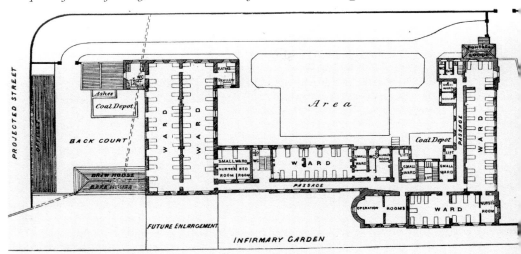

The Infirmary, with addition of Dobson Wing, 1851-1853.

The following year on 6 October 1854, there was a massive explosion in Gateshead resulting in a fire that spread to Newcastle. There were 53 deaths and the Infirmary received 58 in-patients, of which 15 died, and 63 outpatients within a period of four hours. The new Accident Room, which had been opened two days previously, as well as the new wards of the Dobson Wing were utilised for the reception of the casualties. According to Mr Bolton, House Surgeon at the time, pupils and students volunteered their services and patients, who were able to do so, assisted the nurses in caring for the casualties. It was just two weeks after this fire that on 21 October Florence Nightingale took 38 nurses to the military hospital in Scutari, Turkey.

In the Infirmary's Annual Report of 1854, Elizabeth's salary was unchanged from that which Eleanor Pattison had received in 1825, i.e. £42 per annum, whilst the expenditure on the salaries of the Nurses and other servants now amounted to £228.

The Special Court of the Governors of the Infirmary in May 1855 reported with regret the resignation of the late excellent matron of the Infirmary, Mrs Dowson. The following month, in Haltwhistle, Elizabeth married Mr Richard Gibson Kyle, an architect from Durham and formerly of Newcastle. By the time of the 1861 census the couple and their son were living in Tynemouth Terrace, Tynemouth. Elizabeth died in Gateshead early in 1865 leaving one son, Alfred Gibson, who had been born in the spring of 1856. He, like his father, became an architect.

Timeline

1849   Robert Stephenson's High Level Bridge was completed, enabling the railway line from London to reach Newcastle – since 1837 the service was halted at Gateshead.

1850   The Infirmary's Annual Report published in booklet form for the first time, providing more detail than had previously been included in the previous reports of two or three pages.

1851   The College of Medicine became the medical faculty of the University of Durham

1851   Population of Newcastle 87,000.

1854   There were 9453 houses in Newcastle and of these 8032 were without lavatories

---

[1]Hospitals visited in 1851: Manchester Infirmary, the Liverpool and Birmingham Hospitals, the London Hospital, the Middlesex Hospital, St Thomas's and St George's Hospitals. John Dobson also visited the new hospital in Brussels.

ELIZABETH M RONEY
Matron 1855-1860

Elizabeth Milcha Roney was the eldest daughter of Captain James Turner of Mossville, Belfast. She married Alexander Roney on 5 May 1835 in St Anne's Church, Belfast; her father having died before this. By the time of the 1851 census Elizabeth was matron of the Newcastle Gaol and living with her 13-year-old niece Cecelia Blanche Mitchell who was the daughter of Elizabeth's sister Victoria. Victoria and her husband Thomas had moved from Belfast to Scotland following Cecelia's birth in 1839; unfortunately they had both died by 1847, after which time Elizabeth assumed responsibility for Cecelia. Although apparently still married it is uncertain where Elizabeth's husband Alexander was at this time.

In May 1855 Elizabeth was appointed Matron at a Special Court of the Governors of the Infirmary. She had been nominated by Alderman Dodds, who reported that Elizabeth, currently Matron of the Borough Gaol, was a fit and proper person to fill the office of Matron. She had been in post for five years and from his personal observation he could testify to the ability with which she had discharged her duties. He had no doubt that she would give satisfaction if appointed and had great pleasure in proposing her. This motion was seconded by Captain Weatherley, who as a member of the Gaol Committee also testified to the exertions and abilities displayed by the candidate. Having also for many years been connected with the Committee of the Infirmary, he knew something of the requirements of the charity, and he believed that in electing Elizabeth Roney they would be putting the right person in the right place! Another candidate, Mrs Banks, was proposed by Mr Bargate and this nomination was seconded by Mr G N Clark, surgeon. Two other candidates from "a distance" had sent addresses and very satisfactory testimonials but neither was proposed. On the basis of a ballot, Elizabeth was appointed with 77 votes against the 54 in favour of Mrs Banks.

The Statutes and Rules for the Infirmary were revised again in 1855, but those for the Matron were changed very little from 1801. However this would be the last time that the Court of Governors took responsibility for electing the Infirmary's Matron, with responsibility passing to the House Committee.

In November 1856 there was a lengthy and glowing report in the Newcastle Journal of a reporter's visit to the Infirmary. The visit was extensive, taking in the library, museum, hall, chapel, surgery, dispensary, laboratory, brew-house, bake-house, kitchen, accident room, waiting room and consultation rooms as well as the wards. The Accident Room was just to the left of the Porter's Lodge and during the previous nineteen months a total of 888 unannounced accident cases had been received. It was noted that from the hall a door led into the garden, apparently with a pleasing view to the south and the railway viaduct! Steps led down to a garden with a fountain in the central point with flowers shrubs and a grassy area, all of which could be enjoyed by those patients well enough to access it. In inclement weather patients could take exercise in the gallery of the original building. Fresh bread was made in the bake-house, and ale brewed in the brew-house, which also had a large furnace supplying the hospital with hot water.

The wards in the Dobson Wing were reported to be planned and furnished according to the latest and best standards; they were heated by open fireplaces and it was noted that the bedsteads were iron and that the mattresses were now horsehair rather than flock. Each ward had a nurse's room, bathroom and scullery. Elizabeth, and the nurses, who under her superintendence seemed to be very kind and attentive to the wishes of the patients, were given credit for the admirable condition of the hospital. The reporter returned another day to witness two operations performed under chloroform anaesthesia, noting that there were also about thirty 'medical pupils' in attendance.

Entrance to the old infirmary

The Report for 1858 gives the Matron's Salary as £50 for the year, and the annual outlay for the salaries of nurses and servants combined was just in excess of £296. However the old order of nursing was heading for change, heralded not least by the publication in 1859 of Florence Nightingale's Notes on Nursing and Notes on Hospitals. Within the next decade the tensions between the House Committee and the Medical Staff would eventually lead to moves which would revolutionise nursing in the Infirmary.

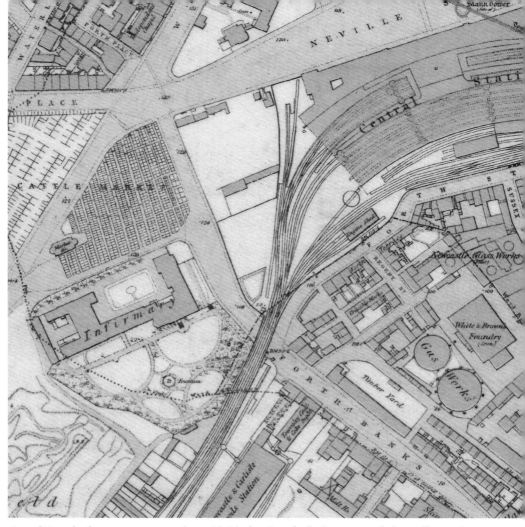

1st edition Ordance survey map from 1864 showing the Infirmary and the cattle market

Elizabeth's resignation was received early in 1860. Early in February the Committee of the Governors of the Newcastle Infirmary had passed a resolution *"that the thanks of the House Committee be given to Mrs Roney for the very efficient and satisfactory manner in which she has discharged the various and onerous duties of her office, with their best wishes for her future welfare and happiness"*.

By this time the post of Matron had once more been advertised in the local press, noting that the appointment would rest with the House Committee and that according to the Statutes of the Charity, candidates must not be more than 45 years of age at the time of appointment, be free from the burden of children and the care of a family. Applicants must leave with the House Committee, testimonials of their qualification and character. Particulars as to the duties and the office, and salary could be obtained on application.

In October 1860 there was an announcement in the local press reporting that

Elizabeth Roney had been elected Matron of Sheffield General Infirmary; the post having been advertised at a salary at £42 including board and lodgings. The 1861 census identified her in Sheffield as Elizabeth Mitchel Roney, a widow aged 49 years (11 years younger than she was in the 1851 census), born in Belfast and Matron of Sheffield General Infirmary. She was only in post for 10 months, before her post was re-advertised in September 1861. Later that year in December 1861 she was unsuccessful in her application for a Matron's post in Northampton.

By the end of 1882, when she signed her will, Elizabeth was living in Belfast where she died aged 69 years in July 1888. The announcement of her death in the local press described her as the daughter of the late Captain Turner of Malone. Probate valued her estate at £118:17s and the beneficiary of her will was her niece Cecelia Blanche, who had married William John Pollard, a clothier and outfitter, in January 1860 and moved to Crook, County Durham. Following William's death, Cecelia married George Lister, a builder, in 1892. Celia died in Crook in 1911 and her son James Hertford Pollard, also a clothier and mercer, died in Crook in 1939 leaving over £20,000.

Timeline

1856 The establishment of the University of Durham licence in Medicine

1858 The Medical Register was established

1859 Another first for Newcastle - the world's first dog show was held in the Newcastle Corn Exchange. It was organised by a gun-maker and enthusiast for gun dogs. There were two classes – one for pointers and one for setters!

MARY COOKE
Matron 1860-1871

Mary Cooke was the second of seven children born around 1830 to John and Ann Cooke from Dissington, near Newburn in Northumberland. Her father was a gardener. The 1851 census recorded Mary as a "*lady's maid*" living with a family in Whickham. At the time of the 1871 census Mary was presumably on leave as she was visiting her older sister Eliza Ann and brother-in-law James Crossley Eno[1] at their home in Chopwell. Eno it will be recalled had been a dispenser at the Infirmary and by this time was a chemist in Newcastle; he subsequently became renowned for his Eno's Fruit Salts. It was noted in the local press in February 1860 that Miss Mary Cooke had been elected Matron to the Newcastle Infirmary. Her salary was £49. 4s. per annum

A review of the Infirmary's census returns for 1841, 1851 and 1861 indicate that Mary Cooke inherited a situation where the number of nurses in post had remained static for at least twenty years with 9 nurses in post. No one nurse appeared more than once across these censuses although it will be noted that the trend was for the recruitment of younger women.

Census Year	Age Range in Years	Average Age in Years
1841	35-65	49+
1851	30-75	42.7
1861	26-61	37

Table 9. Comparison of the age range of the nursing staff, 1841-1861

Up until 1865 the only mention in the Infirmary's Annual Reports relevant to nursing was the name of the Matron, but that year it was reported that 11 nurses were employed by the Infirmary. At this time they would be providing twenty-four hour care for up to 175 in-patients, supported by a couple of "*scrubbers*" who had recently been introduced to the Infirmary staff. Visitors to the Infirmary were at this time required to leave their shoes at the lodge "*so that the wards may be injured as little as possible by the passage of visitors*".

Mary's tenure as Matron, however, was a period of transition for nursing not least as a consequence of the growing influence of Florence Nightingale both in respect of raising the status of nurses and her thoughts on hospital design and sanitation.

The Nightingale School of Nursing, St Thomas's Hospital

In 1855 a public subscription was launched as a tribute to the work of Florence Nightingale's work in the Crimean War. Miss Nightingale, who by this time was committed to establishing nursing as a socially acceptable calling for educated women, was determined to devote this fund to the training of nurses. She took her proposals to St Thomas's Hospital where the Nightingale School of Nursing, funded by the Nightingale Fund Council, opened on the 9 July 1860 with 15 Probationers, aged between 25 and 35 years. The Nightingale Fund paid the Hospital for any expenses incurred in respect of the Probationers and also remunerated those staff involved in their training.

There were eventually two categories of Probationers; the ordinary probationer from the "common classes" received free board and lodgings, including tea, sugar and laundry, and a certain amount of outer clothing along with an annual allowance of £10 per year; and the Lady Probationers or "Specials", who were upper class women with some education. Some of the latter received no salary; others received a small salary; whilst others paid either £30 or £52 a year for their board and lodging. All were under the charge of the Matron and Lady Superintendent, Mrs Sarah Wardroper, and received instruction from the Sisters and the Resident Medical Officer. They were lodged in a separate Home, under the supervision of a Home Sister, and were provided with their own sleeping cubicle whilst sharing a common dining room.

At the end of the year, and providing that their training had been found satisfactory, the Probationers' names were entered on a register kept by the Nightingale Fund and this was used for providing recommendations to other institutions. It became the practice, however, for St Thomas's to take some of the nurses onto the staff of the Hospital after their year in training to give them further experience. The philosophy of the Training School was not to train women for private nursing, but rather to send out trained nurses to 'colonise' those hospitals applying for them; thus the Nightingales signed a four-year contract (subsequently three years) agreeing that they would take employment in a public hospital or wherever they were directed by the Fund Committee. Liverpool Royal Infirmary, in 1862, Liverpool Workhouse Infirmary in 1865, and Edinburgh Royal were notable institutions to benefit from this scheme, all opening up their own training schools. Other Nightingales were going farther afield to Upsala in Sweden, Sydney in Australia, Montreal in Canada, and Philadelphia in America. Notably those "Specials" who agreed to pay £52 a year for their board and lodging were not required to sign a contract. Two of the Nightingales would eventually be appointed Matrons at the Newcastle Infirmary.

The influence of Florence Nightingale also coincided with developments in prevention, diagnosis and treatment as the medical profession was becoming more structured. The catalyst for change in the Infirmary arose from the increasing concern, over a period of eighteen months about an epidemic of erysipelas and "Hospital Gangrene" amongst the surgical patients. In line with Miss Nightingale's thinking, in an attempt to improve the cleanliness of the wards, the Infirmary's floors were planed and saturated with linseed oil, varnished, allowed to harden and then polished in preference to washing with soap and water.

The view of the medical staff was that the infection rates reflected defects in the organisation of the Infirmary, and culminated in Dr Charles Gibb, honorary surgeon, undertaking a survey of the sixteen largest metropolitan and provincial hospitals requesting information regarding the nursing departments in each hospital. This brought to a head tensions between the Infirmary's Medical and House Committees as they juggled with financial pressures. The conflict was eventually brought to the attention of the Anniversary Court of Governors held in April 1868, following letters written by both Dr Gibb and his surgical colleague Dr George Yeoman Heath. Both letters referred to the quantity of nurses (now 13) and the quality of nursing within the Infirmary.

The returns indicated that amongst the hospitals surveyed there was "roughly" a ratio of one nurse to five patients, whilst in the Infirmary it was one nurse to thirteen patients. Dr Gibb gave an example in his letter of the current situation on two of the surgical wards, as shown in Table 10.

	Number of beds	Day Nurses	Night Nurses
Low Flat	60 surgical beds in 5 wards	2	1
Middle Flat	33 male surgical in 3 wards	2	0

Table 10 Nurse staffing levels on the surgical wards, 1868

He also provided details of the condition of the 56 patients in the Low Flat, as shown in Table 11:

Patients with	Total	Bed-ridden	Partially Ambulant	Fully Ambulant
Broken Limbs	6	5	1	
Amputated Limbs	5	5		
Totally Blind	4			4
Other Accidents	41	20	21	
	56	30	22	4

Table 11. Snapshot of in-patients on the Low Flat during April 1868

Dr Charles Gibb

Dr Gibb reported:

"Can it be a matter of surprise that hospital gangrene should appear in these wards when 34 persons so helplessly injured in all the most-shocking forms, and some of the remaining 22 just able to hobble from their beds to the fireside, have to be nursed by two day nurses, with one nurse at night. Are the patients or the nurses to be most pitied? True it is that the patients, who are able, assist those who are not capable of waiting upon themselves, and some more fortunate sufferers are allowed by the medical officers to be nursed by some relative or friend."

"... the medical officers have always allowed a wife, sister, or other female friend of the helplessly ill or injured to take up their residence in the Infirmary, and thus enable the sufferer to have more attentive nursing than the staff of the Infirmary nurses could possibly give them. Indeed whenever I have recommended a patient, helpless from accident, or likely to be so after the performance of some necessary operation, I have always stipulated for the simultaneous admission of a relative or friend to nurse him."

From his findings from the survey Dr Gibb identified two new systems of nursing, i.e.

1. **The St John's House Training Institution for Nurses & Probationers** (established in 1848 by eminent clergy and doctors) had taken over the responsibility for providing King's College Hospital with nurses in 1856; and the All Saints' (Sisterhood) House, also in London, took over the nursing and training at University Hospital in 1862. Charing Cross apparently also used this system of nurse staffing.

2 Meanwhile the **Middlesex Hospital "System for Nursing"** had a Lady Superintendent of Nursing with properly educated and trained nurses, along with probationers. According to the returns, this system had been replicated by the Manchester Royal and Liverpool Royal Infirmaries (this latter Infirmary was one of the first to be colonised in 1862 by three of the first set of probationers to graduate from the Nightingale Training School, St Thomas's Hospital). The report from Leeds noted that "we have a Superintendent and staff of nurses now training at St Thomas's Hospital under the Nightingale Fund Committee" to take charge of the new hospital about to be opened.

This prompted the Chairman at the Anniversary Court to state that he had no hesitation in reporting that over the eight years of Miss Cooke's service her…

"…conduct had been most able and exemplary. She was intelligent and uniformly assiduous in her station, and respectful in her demeanour to every person with whom she came in contact."

The Chairman was not aware that any governor could bring any charge against the matron for uncivility, neglect, or inattention, and on her behalf he thought right to say:

"Should it be the pleasure of the governors to remove her from her situation, she would leave it with much regret, but with inward satisfaction that she had faithfully done her duty and she would have little difficulty in obtaining a situation equally, if not superior, to that she now holds"

As was the custom in those days these events were fully reported in the local press which no doubt added to the challenges Mary had to face as the old order was under ever closer scrutiny and the demands for the training and education of nurses escalating.

As a consequence the Medical Board was tasked to inquire as to what improvements, if any, should be made and in due course the Board submitted a report to the House Committee which after careful consideration resolved:
1.   To adopt in the first place their recommendation as to the number and distribution of the nurses, with the following proviso – to do so subject to such modifications as may be found expedient to meet the necessity of providing sufficient accommodation for their sleeping apartments, and subject also to the patients being restricted to such a number as may not embarrass the financial position of the hospital. The recommendations of the Medical Board are embodied in Table 12.
2.   To appoint a Superintendent of the Nursing Department, to be under the direction of the medical officers, and subordinate to the Matron, the House Committee retaining the same control over all as at present.

3.	To appoint a sufficient number of scrubbers to be employed to clean the floors daily, subject to the directions of the House Committee

4.	To adopt the recommendation of the Medical Board as to the admission of probationary nurses, subject to such regulations as may be from time to time created.

Wards	No of beds	Head Nurse	Nurses Day	Nurses Night	Total Nurses
Low Flat	64	1	3	2	6
Middle Flat A	32	1	1	1	3
Middle Flat B	32	1	1	1	3
High Flat	65	1	3	1	5
Magdalene	28	1	0	0	1
Superintendent Nurse	-	-	-	-	1
	241	5	8	5	19

Table 12. Medical Board recommendations for nurse staffing, 1868

In August 1868 these resolutions were taken to a Special Court of the Governors for approval. Whilst the report was adopted by the Governors it is interesting to note some of the points raised in discussion all of which was reported in the local press. These must have been difficult times for Mary as her role was central to many of the issues under discussion.

•	The proposed improvements would necessitate a considerable increase in the annual expenditure of £400 or £500, there having already been a recent annual increase of £100 as a consequence of the increased price of the patients' diet. It was noted that "….*in the case of a numerous class (of patients) who came into the Infirmary, diet was found to be one-half of the battle. A large number of people with broken down constitutions entered the hospital, and with them good diet was better than medicine.*"

•	Some concern was expressed that if the new Nurse-Superintendent was under the Matron, the question would arise as to whether she would be much use. It was observed that no house ever got on well if there were two mistresses in it! The Chairman of Governors believed that the Matron must always be supreme in the House and that the present Matron was a most excellent servant.

•	The question was also raised as to whether a Nurse-Superintendent would be necessary if they had an efficient Matron. Diverse views were held regarding the suitability of Mary. It was reported that whilst the medical staff recognised the chief deficiency to be in the Nursing Department they had no fault whatever to find with the Matron, other than that she had too many duties to perform in respect of the economical management of the House. Separating the Nursing from the House Department and placing it under an efficient person would enable Miss Cooke to attend more fully to her other duties. There was a view that so far as economical management of the House was concerned, there would be very great difficulty in getting a person as able as Miss Cooke. However there was also a feeling among some in favour of a new Matron with a much higher standing than the present Matron who would be able to attract a better class of nurses which they could not get under Miss Cooke.

Consequently and reflecting the issues and compromises raised in these debates, in 1868 Miss Jane Dunn, a 36-year-old farmer's daughter from Bishop Auckland was appointed Housekeeper allowing the Matron to attend to more nursing duties. She remained in post until 1875. The following year the Statutes and Rules were once again revised and included for the first time Rules for the Housekeeper.

Rules for the Housekeeper 1869

1. That she shall reside in the House and be subordinate to the Mistress

2. That she shall examine, weigh and measure all the provisions and stores which are brought into the House in order to ascertain their quantity and quality as a check upon those who furnish them and she shall keep a daily account thereof for the use and information of the Matron and through her of the sub-committee; that she shall never suffer any provisions to be carried out of the House; that she shall keep the key of the store-rooms and deliver such of a limited quantity of provisions or stores at once as shall enable her to know that it is consumed by the inmates for the Hospital only and that she shall never suffer any person to have access to the provisions or stores without being herself present in order that none may be purloined.

3. That she shall take charge of all the sheets, clothes, bedding and linen, when the same are in store, and not in use on the wards, and shall see that the same are kept in proper repair and condition and marked as belonging to the Infirmary.

4 That under the Mistress, have the general superintendence of the cooking and washing departments, and of all the female domestics; and shall be responsible to the Mistress for every order and regulation relating to the conduct of the servants in her department being strictly observed.

5 That she shall see that the meals of the Resident Officers of the House are punctually and properly served and that their rooms are kept clean and in proper order.

It will be recognised that, encompassed in these tasks which were delegated from the role of the Matron, there were in embryonic form functions which would in time develop into hospital departments in their own right with distinct responsibilities for housekeeping, supplies, catering, laundry, linen bank and sewing rooms. Thus 1869 proved to be a watershed in the history of nursing in the Infirmary. The revised Rules referred to the Matron as the Mistress, and rather than having the proposed Matron and a Superintendent of Nurses, it had been deemed more expedient to have a Housekeeper subordinate to a 'Mistress'. The responsibility of the Mistress had shifted from the more generic role of managing an increasingly complex household to focus primarily on the nursing aspects of the work of the Infirmary, with nurse training now accepted as part of the function of the hospital. New Rules for the Matron were as follows:

Rule 1 "she is in particular held responsible for the due observance of every order and regulation connected with the wards and Nurses"

Rule 6 "she shall instruct the Nurses how to perform their duties and shall see that the Probationers are so employed as to have opportunities of learning their vocation, and at the same time, to be useful in the nursing of patients."

The 1869 Rules for Nurses also identified four classes of Nurses: Head Nurses, Day Nurses, Night Nurses and Probationers. Unlike the Day Nurses who had to report for duty at 7a.m. until 10p.m. each day, the Probationers were to work only from 8a.m. until 6p.m. Before being permanently engaged the Probationers were taken on trial for a period of three weeks providing they were able to read and write, and could produce a character reference regarding their honesty, sobriety and kindness. Probationers were non-resident and had to bring their dinners with them. For the first time these Rules identified the role of the Head Nurse of each 'flat': they had to attend rounds of the physician or surgeon receiving instructions regarding the diet, medicine and treatment of each patient and attend personally those patients on special diet or treatment.

In 1900 Professor Frederick Page, appointed Resident Medical Officer in 1870, recorded his recollections of nursing in the Infirmary at the time of his appointment:

"There were not any trained nurses in Newcastle, either in or outside the Infirmary. In the Infirmary many of the nurses were of the Gamp order – some of them could neither read nor write - and their sobriety, cleanliness and morality were not above suspicion. No uniform was worn and there were members of the honorary staff, still, who could remember a dirty, ignorant, but kind old woman who had charge of Nos. 7 and 8 Wards, some of the brightest in the house.
I can see her now with her dress tucked up into some slit behind, her frowsy stiff petticoats exposed – her un-gartered grey worsted stockings wrinkled on her legs, and her down-at-heels slippers, waddling from one bed to another with a huge linseed meal poultice

to be kindly and gently applied to a suppurating stump. Poor old soul she did her best, but how awful we should consider her best to be now.

What would the smart nurses we have today think if the greater part of their time was occupied in making poultices of linseed meal, which then was used by the ton? Why some of them could not make a linseed poultice properly - as "old S" could, and I do not suppose a stone of linseed meal is (now) used in the Surgical Wards in a year. The clinical thermometer was only then just coming into use and no nurse was ever trusted to take temperatures the doing of which was far from general. What a contrast now when the temperature of each patient is taken and recorded at least twice daily by a reliable and capable nurse.

The Matron in those days was not a trained nurse – she was clever, most anxious to do her duty – but harassed by over work and quite unnecessary worry. She had to superintend the nurses and their duty, the domestic servants and the porters. There were far too few nurses and most of them were incompetent. They were underpaid and the accommodation provided for them was scandalous, of such a nature that it would have been impossible to secure the services of a better class of women.

Some of the old nurses were curious characters. There was one who used to be on night duty – a little dried up apple-faced old woman, who easily lost her presence of mind. A compound fracture requiring amputation came into one of the side wards during the night, and it was her duty to get things in order. She became confused, lost her head and finally could not be found. It was ascertained she had crawled under the bed, whence she was with some difficulty persuaded to return to duty."

Although by 1870 the number of nurses had risen to eighteen, Dr Heath, on behalf of his surgical colleagues, reported that on the Low Flat there were (still) only two day nurses and one night nurse for sixty patients. That same year an issue had been raised at the Quarterly Court of Governors drawing attention to the poor accommodation afforded to mothers who had to stay with their children, and gave an example of one mother who for some weeks "*had nothing but a wooden settle to rest on at night*".

The efficiency in training as well as the number of the nursing staff was not left out of consideration, and the appointment of a well-educated Superintendent of Nurses, capable of guiding the education of those under her charge was urged upon the Committee. This essential of good nursing staff was provided by the generosity of Mrs Catherine Abbot[2], a lady prominent in Newcastle for her liberal giving, who undertook in 1871 to pay a salary not exceeding £100 per annum for a Superintendent of Nurses for a period of ten years stipulating only that the appointment should be in the hands of the medical officers of the Institution. As a consequence, in April 1871 the Anniversary Court of the Governors approved an alteration of the Statutes so that the House Committee could only approve and dismiss a

Northern Goldsmiths jewellers, 1928

Trained Superintendent of Nursing on the recommendation of the Medical Staff.

In view of the events of the previous three years, it is perhaps not surprising that Mary, at the age 41 years, decided to part company with the Infirmary. The Newcastle Journal in July 1871 reported that Miss Cooke, the able and respected Matron of the House, had sent in her resignation and that the Committee of the Infirmary had passed a resolution accepting her resignation and expressing their appreciation as to the manner in which she had fulfilled the duties of her office.

It is not known whether Mary went on to further employment but according to census records she stayed at a variety of addresses. In 1881 she was staying with a younger male cousin in Middlesbrough, in 1891 she was a lodger in Leazes Terrace, and finally in 1901 she was staying with her sister Sarah who was married to John Mensforth Carr a printer and publisher living in St James Street, Newcastle. Mary died aged 73 years in 1903 at the Hydropathic Establishment in Redcar, Yorkshire. Probate was granted to her brother Thomas Cooke, a banker and property developer, and her effects were valued at just under £2400.

Her brother was a well-known gentleman in Newcastle, having given service as a JP, a City Councillor and, from 1891, as an Honorary Governor of the Infirmary serving on the House Committee. Two of his sons were diamond merchants and jewellers and one of Thomas's most imposing projects was the building in 1892, of Goldsmith's Hall – now the Northern Goldsmiths - on the corner of Pilgrim and Blackett Streets. One of his sons, Fleming Gordon Cooke, was the godson of Mr John Fleming, benefactor of the Fleming Memorial Hospital and two streets, Sidney Grove and Crossley Terrace, near what was the Newcastle General Hospital are named after his other sons. Thomas died in 1914 leaving almost £160,000.

Mary's brother-law James Eno, see footnote 1

Timeline

1860 A new cattle market was opened immediately to the west of the Infirmary on Knox's Field, tripling the number of cows coming into the market each week to 3,000. This development had a detrimental effect on the residents of the Infirmary.

1862 "The Blaydon Races" was first performed by singer-songwriter Geordie Ridley in Balmbra's pub in the Cloth Market. As well as giving "The Infirmary" a mention this Tyneside Anthem also immortalises Dr Charles John Gibb, who served the Infirmary as both resident house surgeon and subsequently as honorary surgeon, work which he supplemented with a private practice in Westgate Street.

"Sum went to the Dispensary an 'uthers to Doctor Gibb's An' sum sought out the Infirmary to mend their broken ribs"

1863 The first children's hospital in Newcastle was opened in Hanover Square.

1870 In December the Workhouse Infirmary opened on what eventually became the site of the Newcastle General Hospital. It had 225 beds in 11 wards arranged around a quadrangle which was open to the south faced Westgate Road.

---

[1] Crossley Eno was born in Barrack Square, Newcastle in 1820 and at the age of 14 years he was apprenticed to a chemist and druggist in the Side. By the time of the 1851 census Eno was working as a dispenser in the Infirmary. Subsequently he took over a pharmacy in the Groat Market describing himself as a Dispensing Chemist and, apparently without any special training, Surgeon Dentist, drawing teeth as well as "stopping" them by inserting gold fillings. Turner & Arnison's book The Newcastle School of Medicine, published in 1934, records how Dr George Arnison had a tooth which Eno had "stopped" for him more than 50 years previously.
Like many of his contemporaries he made products under his own brand-name including Eno's Fruit Salts, which he distributed freely to the captains of ships which traded from Newcastle. This policy resulted in him receiving orders from distant parts of the world. In 1876/8 he required larger premises to accommodate his burgeoning Fruit Salt business and set up a large factory at New Cross, London, living at Wood Hall Dulwich for many years. It is worthy of note that Eno's Fruit Salts are still manufactured to this day by Glaxo Smith Kline.
Throughout his life he maintained an interest in the welfare of the Infirmary becoming an Honorary Life Governor. Following his gift of £9550 to the Queen's Commemoration New Infirmary Fund, Ward 11 in the RVI was named the "J C Eno Ward". In 1908 he donated a further £1000 to endow a bed in the "Eno Ward" in memory of his wife Elizabeth Ann. He died aged 95 years in 1915 leaving in the region of £1.6 million and bequeathing £40,000, duty free, to the RVI.
[2] Mrs Catherine Abbot was the wealthy widow of Mr John George Abbot owner of Messrs Abbot & Co of Gateshead, one of the largest iron and brass founders in the country employing at the time of his death in 1867 some 1200 men. Following her husband's untimely death aged 50 years Mrs Abbot supported several major local charitable projects, notably the founding of the Abbot Memorial Ragged and Industrial Schools in Gateshead as well as the Abbot Memorial Building of the Northern Counties Orphan Institution on the edge of the Town Moor in Newcastle. (Subsequently of course this building became home to the Princess Mary Maternity Hospital.) She donated £5000 towards the cost of the building. Prior to her husband's death in 1865, she and her husband had both made donations of £100 to the Infirmary.

ELIZA SOPHIA BLUCK
Lady Superintendent 1871-1875

Eliza Sophia Bluck, the second daughter of Rev John Bluck and his wife Elizabeth, was born in Bowers Gifford, Essex in June 1828. The Blucks had a large family of boys and girls, with at least two of the boys following in their father's footsteps as priests in the Anglican Church. The children all had a boarding school education. John Bluck died in St. Bartholomew's Hospital following an accident with an omnibus in 1857. In 1861 Eliza Sophia, along with her three sisters, was living in Brighton where her eldest sister, Catherine, was head of a small girls' boarding school. By the time of the 1871 census on 2 April, Eliza Sophia was identified as a Lady Nurse and still living in Brighton with her mother and two of her sisters.

Early in 1871 the Anniversary Court of Governors had accepted the generous offer of Mrs Abbot to provide, for a period of ten years, the salary of a Head Nurse for the Infirmary. During February 1871, and several months before Miss Cooke resigned, four candidates applied for the post of Lady Superintendent with two being interviewed; Eliza Sophia, the *"daughter of a clergyman in the South of England"*, was appointed. It is an interesting reflection of the times that it was the status of her father rather than Miss Bluck's own experience as a nurse that was considered more worthy of reporting. Eliza Sophia took up post in July 1871 on an annual salary of £80, and later that month the House Committee approved her request to supply a distinctive uniform dress for the nurses at an estimated cost of £50.

Records for the Nightingale School of Nursing show that Eliza Sophia, aged 39 years, enrolled as a 'Special' on 10 August 1868. However she discontinued her training on the 8 April 1869, having completed only 191 days on duty, and having been on sick leave for the whole of December with cold, fevers and debility. Her record indicates that she had *"neither the mental or physical powers suitable for hospital employment in any capacity"*, and that she was *"delicate and altogether unsuited to hospital work"*. In spite of this, her monthly personal record sheet[1], whilst never scoring 'excellent' across any of the 19 specified criteria, she was in the main assessed as 'good' or 'moderate'. It is unknown what, if any, employment Eliza Sophia undertook following this, and prior to taking up post in the Infirmary, however in 1872 Dr George Yeoman Heath referred to her as *"our excellent Superintendent of Nursing"*.

Professor Frederick Page, writing in 1900, painted a vivid description of the Infirmary as he remembered it in 1870 when he took up post as senior house surgeon. No doubt this would be very much how Miss Bluck found it on her arrival a year later. The building was uninviting, ugly, desolate and not overly clean, quiet or tidy; the wards and passages were all painted a dismal brown, decorated with a few texts such as "*Without the shedding of blood there is no remission of sins*" and "*Prepare to meet thy God*". The only bit of colour was from the scarlet blankets used as counterpanes.

The waste land to the west of the Forth Banks was partly occupied by wooden shanties which provided overnight shelter every Monday for the drovers and their barking dogs in readiness for the Tuesday cattle market; the Hoppings, a travelling fair still coming annually to Newcastle Town Moor, were held to the east of the Infirmary resulting in deafening noise late into the night causing much disturbance and discomfort for the Infirmary's patients and staff.

Professor Frederick Page

The operating room was on the Top Flat; the primary amputations admitted in the night, however, were sent to the side wards on the Low Flat, when available, unfortunately they were in the most part occupied by patients dying of pyaemia. Consequently the patients were admitted to the Victoria or Percy Wards, where a screen would be put around the bed and the limb was removed by the light of tallow candles stuck in a tin sconce, causing no small distress to 50 other patients. Mortality was about 48%; usually the result of infection. Eventually, pending the provision of a new operating theatre, a lumber room was cleared and furnished with two beds and an operating table. Professor Page noted that abdominal surgery was rarely undertaken at this time.

Another insight into the challenges faced by the Infirmary comes from a letter of petition sent to Parliament in 1874 from the Chairman of the House Committee. It was in response to a Bill proposing to amend the laws relating to the sale and consumption of intoxicating liquors and arguing against any extension of the drinking hours in public houses. In support of their petition the Committee reported that the Infirmary was open at night for the reception and treatment of accident cases and that 70% of such admissions were drunk, with a large proportion of the remaining 30%, whilst not actually drunk, more or less under the influence of liquor! The press cutting below provides a summary of patient activity, including casuals, for a typical week in 1874.

NEWCASTLE INFIRMARY.—The following is the return for the week ending Thursday, April 2:—Patients in the house, 163; admitted during the week, 29; discharged, 39. Out-door patients (by letter) 165, of whom 5 were new cases. Number of casuals treated during the week, 186. Total number of patients treated during the week, 582.

Soon after Miss Bluck's arrival, changes were afoot in the Infirmary with, in 1872, the building of a new operating theatre; the old theatre on the second floor becoming known as the Ovarian Room where only minor gynaecological operations were performed. Other work included the provision of a nurses' dining hall and a women's convalescent ward. It was around this time that improvements to the patients' diet were introduced with the provision of 5 meals a day – this was not common practice in other hospitals at the time and gained the Infirmary praise from no less a place than Guy's Hospital. However, in spite of the Infirmary now offering places for probationer nurses, the lack of skilled nurses was becoming an increasing problem both in and outside the Infirmary.

Advertisements in the local press appeared from time to time during the period 1872 -1874 seeking candidates for the following posts:
•   Assistant Nurses: must be able to read and write, with uniform and washing, salary range £12-£15 per annum.
•   A trained good surgical nurse to superintend and take charge of the male accident wards. Wage £25 per annum with uniform and washing

In a letter to the Newcastle Journal in May 1872, senior surgeon Dr George Yeoman Heath had noted a dearth of educated nursing power in the district, commenting that the Infirmary was unable to recruit or supply skilled and earnest nurses. In identifying a need for trained, efficient and intelligent nurses, he proposed the establishment of a Nurses' Home and Training School similar to establishments elsewhere in the country. This proposal was no doubt influenced in part by the work of the St John's House Training Institution for Nurses' & Probationers, and the All Saints' (Sisterhood) House, as well as the Nightingale Training School for Nurses, which had now been operating for over 10 years. Several other Homes and Training Schools for Nurses had opened in the provinces most notably, according to Heath, in Liverpool where there was one associated with the Royal Infirmary, and Derby. In June the following issues were raised at a meeting held in the Infirmary:

1.   The Infirmary required probationers, but had no accommodation
2.   The district required a central institution from where reliable nurses could be readily procured
3.   There was a need for the provision of a quiet comfortable establishment where ladies and children requiring medical and surgical treatment could be received and skilfully nursed

Heath proposed a House that could accommodate eight to twelve women under the charge of a Mistress who would make a comfortable home where the women would be taken care of. It would not be desirable he thought, to select the probationers from any special class, but that they must be taken from whatever class they could get them. The Mistress, he thought, ought to be an educated person – a lady if possible – capable of giving a certain amount of instruction to the women during their leisure hours, instruction in various things, but not in nursing. It was proposed that the probationers would go to the Infirmary at 8 a.m. and leave again at a sufficiently early hour to get some recreation.

The calling of a nurse was an exceedingly trying one and there should be a certain amount of leisure in order that their health might be retained. It was proposed that as in similar institutions the Home would pay an entrance fee of one or two guineas to the Infirmary for each nurse as a payment for the instruction that they would receive.

The instruction in the Infirmary would be provided by Eliza Sophia, in whom they had an enthusiastic and capable teacher. Practical instruction would also be provided by the head nurses of the wards and the medical staff would also be obliged to give some instruction. He suggested that in the wards of the Infirmary there were opportunities and facilities for the education of nurses which were not to be surpassed, and were only waiting to be utilised. This School for Nurses would be able to supply the Infirmary, the town and district with greater number of better quality nurses.

Heath envisaged that the home would be funded by a combination of public subscription and the charging of fees for supplying nurses to institutions or private homes. The nurses would be supported, lodged, clothed and paid a fixed salary by the home. The proposed resolution "That it is desirable to establish in Newcastle, in connection with the Infirmary, a Home and Training School for Nurses" was carried unanimously, and the composition of a working committee to take the proposal forward and report back in July was agreed.

By the July meeting a Superintendent for the Home had been found. A Miss Marks had offered to superintend the Home having for nine months assisted, on a voluntary basis, her sister in the superintendence of the Derby and

Derbyshire Nursing and Training Association. Currently Miss Marks was assisting her sister who was supervising the nursing and housekeeping at the Durham County Hospital. It was therefore agreed to negotiate for the property at 6 Charlotte Square and the following constitution of the Home was agreed:

• The applicants for admission to the Home shall be persons of good character of fair education and of sound health of mind and body. The age considered desirable is 25 – 40 years.

• That each candidate be required to undergo a month's probation at the Infirmary, and at the close of that period, if found qualified, be bound to the Committee of the House for a time of service extending over three years.

• That the House be opened, for the present, for the admission of a limited number of certificated nurses; and that a book, for the registration of such nurses as are approved by the Committee, be kept at the institution.

• That two trained nurses shall be at once engaged by the Committee of the Institution for the employment in connection with the Home.

• That the general period of training for probationers be one year, and this may either be shortened or extended to eighteen months or two years at the discretion of the Committee. This period of training to be passed in the practice of nursing at the Infirmary. N.B. – The certificate of each nurse connected with the Home should be signed by the Superintendent of Nursing at the Infirmary, the House Surgeon, and one surgeon or physician of the honorary medical staff.

• That the probationers and nurses, while at the Infirmary, shall submit to the rules and regulations of that institution

• That the probationers during the time of their connection with the Home be subject to such rules and regulations as are passed by the Committee.

• That the probationers be paid at the rate of £10 per annum by the Committee of the Home and provided with suitable uniform, and, at the end of their period of probation, be paid at the rate of £16; to be raised to £20, at the discretion of the Committee, after the end of the second year, exclusive of clothing.

• Eight nurses, duly qualified, and desirous of remaining inmates of the Home after the termination of their engagement, shall be eligible to receive wages at a higher rate, but not exceeding £25.

• That the charge made by the Home for an experienced nurse, shall be at the rate, for ordinary and surgical cases, £1 1s per week; for infectious cases, £1 11s 6d per week.

*6 Charlotte Square, the former
Nurses' Home and Training School*

On the 15 August 1872, only three months after it was first proposed, an advert appeared in the local press:

> *"Nurses' Home and Training School[2] - The Committee of the above Institution are now prepared to receive a limited number of respectable young women to reside in the Home, and be trained as nurses. Very great advantages and facilities for becoming thorough and efficiently trained nurses, and constant employment are provided by the Home. – Applications to be addressed "The Nurses' Home and Training School, 6 Charlotte Square, Newcastle" or made personally to the Secretary, Dr Page, at the Infirmary."*

A report of the Anniversary Court of Governors in April 1873 noted that three nurses belonging to the Nurses' Home in Charlotte Square were currently employed in the Infirmary. However, although every effort had been made to recruit an adequate number of suitable nurses to the Infirmary, this had met with only partial success. The great difficulty was getting candidates with the requisite education, mental and moral qualities, as well as a general aptness for the work. *"When such persons are found they are trained with comparative facility, and soon become of great value. Persons of low mental power can never be relied on."*

There was, however, fulsome praise for Miss Margaret Graham[3], who had initially provided cover for Miss Bluck's autumn holiday in 1872, but had then been induced to stay on for a total of seven months performing the duties of an ordinary nurse. Margaret had been a probationer at the University College Hospital and was subsequently *"in full charge of a large ward at the Middlesex Hospital"*. In April 1875, at the time of her appointment to the post of Lady Superintendent and Matron of the Norfolk and Norwich Hospital, she was reported as having been temporary Lady Superintendent at the Newcastle Infirmary on three occasions. Infirmary records indicate that she had been a powerful stimulation to the nursing department, *"and instead of following the usual avocations of persons in her position of life, devoted herself with rare zeal, assiduity, and skill to the alleviation of the sufferings of her fellow creatures."* As she would not accept even her travelling expenses, the Weekly Committee, when it became necessary that she would leave Newcastle, presented her with a bracelet as a small memorial of her residence in the Infirmary along with a copy of the following resolution:

"It is with great regret that the Weekly Committee learn that Miss Graham is about to leave the Infirmary. They cannot allow her to do so without thanking her very heartily for the services she has rendered during the last seven months, assuring her that they have watched with admiration the noble self-devotedness with which she threw herself into the discharge of her arduous duties. Some patients have been restored to health, who to all appearance would have sunk under their severe maladies but for her assiduous and skilful nursing; and many others have been cheered and comforted during the tedious hours of illness by her kind attentions.

The Committee hope that the example which Miss Graham set will induce many other ladies of birth, talent, and education to give themselves to the honourable and blessed work of nursing their fellow creatures in distress. Knowing that Miss Graham would shrink with sensitiveness from any offer of remuneration, the committee yet beg of her that she will accept the accompanying bracelet as a memorial of her residence in the Newcastle Infirmary".

Whilst in Norfolk, Margaret was held in the highest of esteem for the changes she introduced and was credited for playing a major part in the reduction of deaths from pyaemia and erysipelas. Margaret resigned her post in Norfolk early in 1877 on grounds of impaired health brought on by overwork. In April 1877 she married Frederick Page, who had been the Senior House Surgeon during her time at the Infirmary and who would subsequently become Professor of Surgery in Newcastle.

In March 1875 Miss Bluck had been recorded as "very assiduous in her duties", however the relationship between her and the members of both Honorary

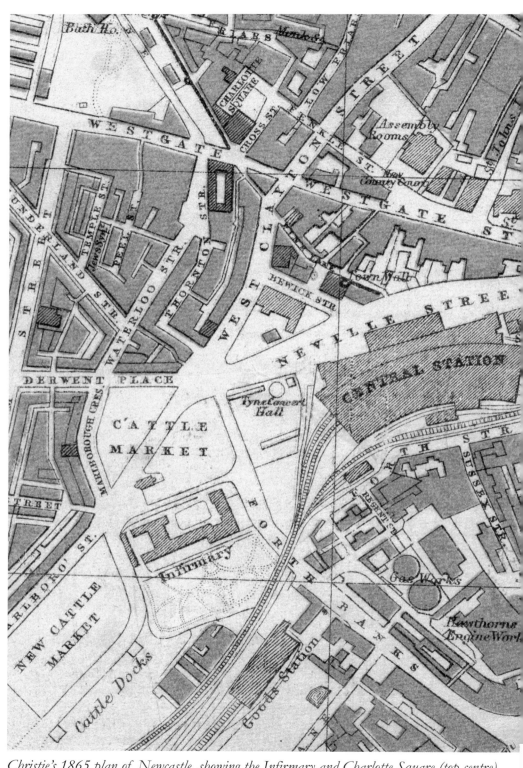

Christie's 1865 plan of Newcastle, showing the Infirmary and Charlotte Square (top centre)

Staff and the House Committees seems to have deteriorated rapidly after this. Early in May she had submitted a request for her sister to stay with her for three month's nurse training in the Infirmary prior to undertaking pastoral work. This request was turned down on the basis that it was against the rules for probationers to live in the Infirmary.

Soon after this the Honorary Staff Committee, but notably without the support of Dr Heath, recommended that Eliza be requested to resign because of concerns about the unsafe condition of the nursing, but "*more especially the relationship of the Superintendent to some of the other officials*". Miss Bluck subsequently submitted a letter of resignation commenting on the inconsistency of the House Committee in respect of the application of the Rules and that she would be working only one month's notice rather than the three months as was expected. She left office early in June without a testimonial, in spite of the House Committee expressing "*their appreciation of her zeal and devotion in fulfilling the duties of Superintendent during the four years she had resided in the Infirmary and her unremitting attention to the patients under her care.*"

Dr George Yeoman Heath

In June 1876 Eliza Sophia's eldest sister Catherine, a governess aged 51 years, was admitted on her brother James's authority, to the Royal Bethlem Hospital. She was admitted as a private rather than a pauper patient, with a three-week history of delusions. Eliza Sophia provided information regarding her sister's behaviour leading up to her admission. Catherine was discharged two years later in June 1878 apparently without improvement. Another sister Sarah Hannah became a Sister of the Poor with the St Mary of Nazareth Anglican Order and worked in a home for the incurables. By 1881 Eliza Sophia was living with her 83-year-old mother in Tunbridge Wells in the same house where she would die at the age of 92 in January 1921. Probate recorded her effects as being valued at £4968.

Timeline

1871 A grand full-dress ball was held in the Assembly Rooms in aid of funds for the Infirmary. There had been instant demand for tickets with over 800 sold for half a guinea each. In addition there were others who paid an increased charge of 15s each at the door.

[1] Probationer's Personal Record Sheet of the Nightingale School of Nursing - the major headings on this related to:
Personal Character: Punctuality, Quietness, Trustworthiness, Personal Neatness & Cleanliness, Ward Management.
Nursing Experience: Dressings, Applying Leeches, Enemas, Management of Trusses & Uterine Appliances, Rubbing, Helpless Patients, Bandaging, Making Beds, Waiting on Operations, Sick Cooking, Keeping the Ward Fresh, Cleanliness of Utensils, Management of Convalescents, Observation of the Sick.
[2] Nurses' Home and Training School: Eighteen months after opening it was reported to have 8 nurses, 3 having been trained entirely at the Infirmary, 2 partially trained and 3 probationers. Sixty requests for nursing care had been received from as far afield as Rothbury and the Isle of Ely. The Nurses' Home and Training School was to continue well into the 20th century, however by 1882 the nursing training arrangements at the Infirmary were such that it no longer required support from this Institution.
[3] Margaret Page (nee Graham) was the daughter of John Graham a renowned calico printer and niece of Professor Graham FRS a distinguished chemist and one time Master of the Mint. According to the 1871 census she had "land in Scotland" and her brother a barrister at the time later became a KC and judge. Margaret died in Newcastle in 1898 aged 50 years, and Frederick in 1919; they had three children.

MARIE ANNE BARRY MACKEY
Superintendent of Nurses 1875-1879

Marie Anne Barry Mackey, born in 1847 at St George, Bermuda, was the first of three children born to Hugh Mackey Jnr and Maria Maine who had been married in Belfast in 1846.

In 1837 her father, *"a gentleman and surgeon"* and son of Hugh Mackey Snr, also a surgeon, was appointed an Assistant Surgeon to the forces. At this time each regiment had its own Assistant Surgeon and Surgeon, and whilst they did not hold a military rank they wore the regimental uniform. Hugh served with the 5th foot regiment (the Northumberland Fusiliers) before being promoted first to Surgeon with the 42nd foot regiment (the Black Watch) and subsequently Staff Surgeon prior to his posting to Jamaica and then Bermuda. Of particular interest are press reports in July 1855 regarding the arrival in Spithead, Portsmouth of the vessel Calphurnia which had left Scutari on 25 April with 151 military invalids and two women on board. Credit for the excellent order of the invalid's berths in the ship, the cleanliness and quality of their bedding, and the order and comfort of the invalids was given to the Staff Surgeon in medical charge – Marion's father Hugh Mackey.

Miss Mackey, photo courtesy of the Royal College of Nursing

It was reported that no ship had either left or returned to Portsmouth in such excellent order, the state of which needed to be seen to be appreciated. Apparently he returned to the Crimea in February 1856 in medical charge of troops for the Crimea. At the time of his death in 1858, aged 44 years, he was Garrison Staff Surgeon in Halifax, Nova Scotia. The family returned to the UK with their mother receiving an army pension of £50 per year whilst Marie Anne and her two siblings received a pension of £12 per annum until the age of 21 years, although that of her "feeble minded" brother would continue throughout his life.

By 1871 Marie Anne, reported to be "*a governess*", was living in Colchester with her mother and brother William. Subsequently between 1872-1873 she served as a probationer nurse at the Bradford Infirmary reporting in an article in the Nursing Record in March 1893 that she had met with considerable opposition from her mother as nursing was not then the fashionable profession it had since become. She also reported:

> "*I had many difficulties to contend with, because being a lady was rather against a nurse then. The work was very rough and heavy.*"

In February 1872 the Bradford Medico-Chirurgical Society had discussed the expediency of establishing an institution for the training of nurses. By April the Matron, Miss Jelly, and nurses had been recruited. The Institution was soon advertising trained nurses for monthly, medical and surgical cases. The Yorkshire Post reported that at the first annual meeting of the Bradford Nurses' Institution in June 1873 that there were two probationer nurses at the Bradford Infirmary and another four employed in other hospitals. Advertisements for probationers specified that candidates must be between the ages of 22 and 30 years and able to read and write.

It is unknown where Marie Anne was employed following her time at the Bradford Infirmary, however it seems that the rapid promotion of suitable "lady nurses" was the order of the day. She was the successful candidate from a field of fourteen applicants for the post vacated by Miss Bluck and took up post in July 1875.

Marie Anne's time at the Infirmary coincided with a number of changes worthy of mention. Firstly, in order to keep the labour class of servants (scrubbers and washers) as respectable as possible, it was deemed necessary to provide them with on-site accommodation. Secondly, in order to reduce tensions between the resident officials, the Senior House Surgeon was given general control over the Superintendent of Nurses and the Housekeeper. There were three Housekeepers during Marie Anne's term in office, Misses Dunn, Rimington[1] and Waters[2]. This was reported as successfully introduced and considerably reducing the work of the House Committee – however further 'restructuring' would soon follow! The other major change came as a result of the introduction of antiseptic methods.

By this time there was a growing awareness that microbes were the source of infection and of the importance of antisepsis in its prevention. In 1874 Dr George Thomas Beatson was appointed senior house surgeon. He had previously served under Professor Joseph Lister in Edinburgh and brought his antiseptic techniques to the Infirmary with the effect of greatly reducing infection rates. The Annual Report for 1876 reported that carbolic acid was used to wash wounds, the surgeon's hands, and instruments and sponges were also disinfected with it. Additionally, throughout an operation the air surrounding the wound was sprayed with the acid and all dressings were carefully impregnated with it. The cost of these new techniques had in part, been offset by a massive reduction in the three tons of linseed meal previously required each year to make poultices for infected wounds. During the years 1875 and 1876 no cases of pyaemia or other serious "*hospital disease*" were recorded in the Infirmary.

The impact of the antiseptic system had the effect of greatly increasing the workload of the Infirmary due to the revolution in surgical practice. Marie Anne was therefore in post at a time when the number of operations performed in the Infirmary began to increase at a quite dramatic rate. Between the years 1876 and 1884 these rose from 297 to 908, resulting in yet another demand for more beds. By this time the Infirmary was accessing accommodation for convalescing patients with facilities in both Whitley Bay and Killingworth.

Photo: Tom Yellowley

A Lister carbolic spray which was used in the old Infirmary

In June 1876 following a disagreement between Dr Beaston and Miss Mackey, and involving a nurse, the House Committee reported: *"an amount of laxity and indiscretion has been shown to exist among some of the chief officers which has called forth strong expressions of condemnation from many members of the Committee who consider such conduct to be highly unbecoming and deserving of censure".*

In February 1877, another more recently appointed senior house surgeon, Dr Williamson along with two nurses, made a complaint about the manner in which Miss Mackey performed her duties. This resulted in her being given leave of absence pending an investigation. In the subsequent hearing Miss Mackey was supported by her cousin who had the opportunity to cross-examine the witnesses, including another two nurses who were supportive of the Superintendent, resulting in Miss Mackey returning to duties. That year Miss D'Arcy[3] of Winchester Hospital provided cover for Miss Mackey's summer holiday and then stayed on as Housekeeper pending the appointment of Miss Waters in August 1877.

The Infirmary meanwhile continued to take up to four probationers from the Nurses' Home and Training School with training from December 1876 being increased from one to two years. According to a Finance Committee Report in January 1878, during the period 1875 to 1877, there were 29 nursing staff with an average of 186 beds. Table 13 illustrates the grades of nurses identified at that time:

Grade	Number
Superintendent of Nurses	1
Head Nurses	6
Assistant Nurses	2
Night Nurses	7
Probationers	13
	29

Table 13 Grades of nurses identified for the period 1875-1877

The Committee expressed some concern at the large proportion of young, and therefore inexperienced nurses. A month prior to this report there had been an advert in the local press for two trained night nurses at a salary of £18 per annum.

In December 1878 a decision was made to replace the House Steward of the Infirmary by a House Governor to have overall responsibility for all of the non-medical aspects of the hospital. It is unknown whether this had any bearing on Miss Mackey's decision to resign in January 1879. From 1881 she worked firstly at the Leicester Infirmary and from 1883 to 1887 she was Matron at the Lock Hospital, Colchester. At this point Marie Anne felt that she needed *"to get her hand in again for general nursing"*, and went on to 'The

London' as Night Sister; she was there for the year 1887-1888 at which time Miss Eva Lückes was the Matron. Like Florence Nightingale, Miss Lückes was very much against the proposed registration of nurses. Marie Anne however thought differently as is evidenced by her membership of the General Council of the British Nurse's Association (BNA) which had been founded in 1887 and which, under the influence of Ethel Bedford Fenwick[4], was actively campaigning for the registration of nurses.

It was about this time that Marie Anne was recruited by Mr T Mark Hovell, FRCS, aural surgeon at the London Hospital to become Sister-in-Charge/Matron to the Hospital for Diseases of the Throat, Golden Square, London. This was a small hospital comprising 26 beds in three wards treating adults and children. Mr Hovell was also a member of the Royal British Nurses' Association, serving on its General Council. By this time Marie Anne seems to have shown a preference to be called "Marion".

The hospital in Golden Square had some high profile visits during Marie Anne's tenure, including a number from the Empress Frederick of Prussia, Queen Victoria's first born daughter Victoria, who dedicated the children's ward to the memory of her 11-year-old son who had died as a consequence of diphtheria.

Described in the Nursing Record variously as "courageous" and "energetic" Miss Mackey attended the birthday party of the British Nurses Association in the Princes' Hall in December 1890. Meanwhile the BNA had established its own voluntary register with Marie Anne registering in March 1890 – number 493. The following year, by which time the Association had been granted Royal status, Marie Anne was present at the fourth birthday of the Association, and along with other members of the General Council, was presented with the Association's silver badge by Her Royal Highness Princess Christian, daughter of Queen Victoria. In total 350 silver and bronze badges were presented.

In July 1891 the Nursing Record featured a pen and ink sketch of Marie Anne and in 1893 she received from the founder of the hospital in Golden Square a silver medal inscribed "Sister Mackey - in appreciation of special service from November 1890 to April 1891 from Sir Morell Mackenzie". This related to the thirty cases at the hospital who received the Koch treatment for throat consumption and lupus.

In February 1893 she hosted a concert at Golden Square for patients and nurses and was praised in the nursing press for the assiduous care with which she looked after those present. The following month there was a three-page report, including a photograph, in the Nursing Record of an interview with Miss Mackey.

Ill health prompted Marie Anne's retirement from "Golden Square" in 1894 and she died in January 1906, having lived the last years of her life at Athol Mansions in Lambeth. Her estate was valued at £1224 and probate was granted to her cousin, a barrister at law, Archibald John Mackey former pupil of Westminster School and a graduate of Trinity College, Cambridge.

Timeline

1877   The Ear Nose and Throat Hospital opened in Clayton Street

1877   Publication of 'Hints for Hospital Nurses', arranged by R. Williams and A Fisher. Both were products of the Nightingale School of Nursing and had subsequently worked at the Edinburgh Royal Infirmary, but at the time of printing Miss Williams was Matron of St. Mary's Paddington and Miss Fisher Matron of the Fever Hospital in Newcastle. Miss Fisher was subsequently appointed Matron of Addenbrooke's Hospital in Cambridge, before moving on to Birmingham General Hospital, and finally to Philadelphia where her memory has been long revered

1878   The Chest Hospital opened in Blackett Street

---

[1] Sophia Ruth Alice Rimington was born in Newcastle and trained at Leeds General Hospital 1870-1873. She resigned her post in the Infirmary having been appointed Matron of the Guest Hospital, Dudley from 1877 to 1879, and subsequently as Matron of the General Hospital Nottingham from 1879-1892. In her later years she opened "a high class boarding house" for convalescents in Brighton.
[2] Miss Waters, from London, was selected from amongst the 31 candidates who had applied for the post of Housekeeper.
[3] Miss Lousia M D'Arcy trained in 1869 under Mrs Freeman, a Nighingale, at the Royal County Hospital, Winchester and had been a Sister there since 1874. In 1878 she was appointed Matron to Grimsby Hospital, and subsequently became Matron to Winchester College
[4] Ethel Bedford Fenwick: See Appendix 2

ELIZA PEEL
Lady Superintendent of Nurses and Matron, 1879-1884

Eliza Peel was the third of eight children born to George and Margaret Kennedy; she was born in Sussex during the last quarter of 1839. In 1841 her father was described as a carpenter, however by 1851 he was a cabinet maker employing 11 men and two apprentices. Eliza married James Peel early in 1860 and at the time of 1861 census the couple were living in Brighton and James was recorded as being a Hospital Dispenser; they had a five-week-old son.

By 1871 James and Eliza were living in St Pancras, London with three children: James, Robert and Frederick aged 10, 7, and 4 years respectively. James senior was described as a 'medical dispenser (chemist)'. James died in the early months of 1875 aged 43 years and about this same time James the eldest son joined the merchant navy as an apprentice. By the time of the 1881 census Robert was an apprentice tailor and Frederick was at boarding school in Bedford.

Eliza was one of 28 candidates who had applied for the post of Lady Superintendent of Nurses and Matron at the Infirmary in January 1879, having undertaken nurse training at the London Hospital. There had been a nurse training school at The London since 1873 whilst Annie Swift, the predecessor to Miss Eva Lückes, was Matron. The training at that time consisted of working on the wards for one year after which, and without taking an examination, probationers were considered to be trained nurses.

At interview Eliza had indicated that she was happy to be in-charge of housekeeping in addition to her responsibilities as Superintendent of Nurses and therefore be 'Mistress of the House' under the House Governor. She commenced duties in February 1879 and the following month, on a salary of £300, sufficient to attract *"a gentleman of education, social position, and high moral and religious tone of mind"*, a House Governor was appointed with responsibility for the control and management of the whole non-professional affairs of the Hospital.

One of the changes that the House Governor introduced was to dispense with the post of Miss Waters as Head of the Household and place all the female servants once again under the charge of the Superintendent of Nurses. Thus the Housekeeper was replaced by an Assistant Housekeeper, Miss Jane Ann Alexander[1], and responsible to Eliza Peel, who was now entitled Superintendent of Nurses and Matron. By April 1880 Eliza's salary had been increased from £80 to £100 per annum.

The 1881 Census, recorded 214 patients in the Infirmary along with 19 domestic servants including three porters, and 28 nurses. There were two house surgeons, three clinical assistants as well as Mrs Peel and the Assistant Housekeeper. As Table 14 illustrates, the age profile of the nursing staff had changed from its previous reliance on older widowed woman, an indication that nursing was becoming a much more fashionable career for young single women.

Age in Years	1881 No of Nurses	Marital Status	1871 No of Nurses	Marital Status
18-20	7			
21-25	12		2	
25-30	4	1 widow	1	1 married
31-35	2	1 married	2	2 widows
36-40	1		4	2 widows
41-45			1	1 widow
46-50	1	1 widow	3	2 married
				2 widows
51-55			3	1 widow
56-60			2	1 widow
61-64	1			
64				
Totals	28	25 Single	18	6 Single
		1 Married		3 Married
		1 Widow		9 Widows

Table 14. Comparison of the age profile of the nurses resident at the Infirmary, 1871 and 1881

The 1881 Annual Report commented that the nursing department had been maintained in a state of unusual efficiency under the excellent management of Mrs Peel and that during the summer, the nurses in detachments had been provided with excursions into the country. It was during Mrs Peel's term of office in 1882 that it was reported the first objective of the Nurse' Home and Training School to provide accommodation for probationer nurses was no longer an issue as the nursing arrangements at the Infirmary had, at considerable expense, been perfected.

New Rules for the Infirmary staff were published in 1883 and these included some strengthening of those for the Matron. Her responsibilities were now shifting from a purely housekeeping role to that with stipulated responsibilities for the nursing care of the patients. Matron was now given additional responsibilities, as follows:

- Accompany the honorary physician and honorary surgeon on their visits to the wards.

- Visit the wards as frequently and for as long periods of time as her other duties would permit, ensuring that the prescribed medicines were punctually and regularly administered by the nurses; that the wants and comforts of the patients were duly attended to and that they were treated with proper care and tenderness by the nurses; and that the patients' sheets were changed every seven days or oftener if necessary (it had previously been every fourteen days)

- Treat the patients with good nature and civility, and to ensure that any unkindness or neglect of the nurses towards the patients was dealt with.

- Superintend the nurses in the performance of their duties; and from time to time, instruct them in how to perform their duties, and see that the probationers are so employed as to have opportunities of learning their vocation, whilst at the same time, be useful in the nursing of patients.

- Attend, as far as practicable, the admission of all persons accidentally injured, and see that the beds and every other accommodation be provided without delay.

130 years after the Infirmary opened the role of patients in supporting the work of the hospital was still a feature of the Rules for the Matron. All of the patients' bedding had to be aired in the courtyard every fourteen days and those patients approved by the medical staff were expected to assist with this task.

The Infirmary benefitted from support of local people in many different ways and a report in the Newcastle Courant in late December 1883 gave an example of this. A group of Christian ladies who called themselves the 'Infirmary Singing Band', usually visited the Infirmary every Wednesday afternoon to sing to the patients, but on Monday 24th December they had gathered unannounced on the wards at 9pm to sing Christmas Carols. The ladies of the Band had also prepared Christmas Cards and letters to be given to each patient on Christmas morning.

It was also reported that on Christmas Day the patients in the children's ward each received a bun and an orange at breakfast, provided by the wife of Dr (George Haliburton) Hume, Honorary Surgeon to the Infirmary, and grandfather of Cardinal Basil Hume. Later all the patients enjoyed a dinner of "*prime roast beef and plum pudding in unstinted quantities*" with more oranges being distributed to each patient for dessert.

In March 1884 a patient in the Infirmary developed small-pox and was transferred to the Small-pox Hospital where he died. Those who had been in contact with the patient were isolated and re-vaccinated. In spite of these precautions seven patients, two nurses, a porter, a scrubber, and two students all developed the disease and were also transferred to the Small-pox Hospital. All survived.

It was about this time that Rules for the Head Night Nurse, who was on duty from 9pm until 9 am, were introduced.

George Haliburton Hume

She was expected to visit each ward every hour. Probationers and Assistant Nurses reported for duty at 7am and the Head Night Nurse gave a report at 9am to the Matron, the House Physician and the House Surgeon.

Eliza resigned her post in November 1884 to take up a post in London. The only further information about her was that in 1891 she was a boarder living on her own means with a couple in Wimbledon, and by 1901 she was living in Harrogate with her son Robert, a tailor and habit maker. Eliza died in Worthing in April 1907, her address being the same as where, in 1911, her son Robert, now described as a "gentleman", was living with two servants. She left the princely sum of £47, but Robert who died in 1914 left almost £40,000. The younger son, Frederick, has been identified in both the 1901 and 1911 census as living in South Shields and employed as a mechanical draughtsman. By 1911 he had been married for 25 years. He and his wife, who was born in Newcastle, had seven children and lived in an eight-roomed house. There is not further information regarding Eliza's eldest son James.

Timeline

1882   The Smallpox Hospital opened on the Town Moor.

1883   The founding of the Newcastle Cathedral Nursing and Loan Society.

[1]Jane Ann Alexander was described in the 1881 Census as "Assistant Housekeeper", single, aged 32 years and having been born in South Shields. The entry also describes her as a school teacher. No further information is known.

CATHERINE PAYNE BALKWILL
Matron 1884-1889

Catherine Payne Balkwill was born in Plymouth in 1843. She was the youngest of six children born to Joseph Hancock Balkwill and Ann Payne. Joseph was a chemist and druggist working in the business which the Balkwill family had taken over in 1826. The Messrs Balkwill & Company (Chemists) Ltd continued trading until 1974. Joseph's wife Ann assumed control of the business after his death the year following Catherine's birth. Two of Catherine's brothers subsequently took over the business. According to the 1871 census Catherine was in Luton and a "companion" to a couple and their two sons. A decade later she was reported to be the Matron of the Mildmay Medical Mission Hospital.

Mildmay Medical Mission

The Mildmay Medical Mission Hospital had been opened in 1877 as one of the outreach missions of the protestant Deaconess Institution. The Institution was founded in 1860 by the Rev William Pennefather and originally based in Barnet. In 1864 it moved to Mildmay Park in Islington. The women, predominately from the upper classes, were self-funded and received two years of theoretical and practical training for a role that was a cross between nursing and what we now know as social work. They wore a distinctive crinoline uniform and bonnet, which offered them protection in even the roughest of areas.

On completion of training the deaconesses, who could number 200 at any given time, worked in one of the 20 outlying missions, mostly in London, and all established in response to requests from parish priests. The nursing branch was started in 1866 when two of the Mildmay deaconesses responded to a call from the vicar of St Philip's Church in Bethnal Green to care for the sick during the cholera outbreak. Whilst Mildmay Park was described as "run down" Bethnal Green was *"...an area in which the police would not venture alone. It was a place of prostitutes, drunkenness, violence, nefarious street urchins and filth"*. The deaconesses' work in Bethnal Green continued and in 1874 the Mildmay Medical Mission was established there to be followed, three years later by the opening of the Mildmay Medical Mission Hospital in a converted warehouse behind Shoreditch Church. This was the first London mission hospital and comprised 27 beds in three wards with one doctor, three nurses and five deaconesses in training.

It was from the Mildmay Medical Mission Hospital that Catherine, now aged 39 years, moved to the Infirmary late in 1884. She had been one of 35 applicants for the post[1] and like her predecessor, was paid an annual salary of £100. Two of Catherine's paternal aunts had married men from the North East and, according to the 1881 census, her Aunt Sarah and a cousin were living in Summerhill Grove, in Westgate Newcastle. It was reported by the chaplain to the Infirmary in 1885 that Catherine had introduced short services for prayer and reading of the scriptures every evening, and that these were well attended by the nurses.

In spite of the move north it appears that Catherine retained her link with Mildmay Park Institute, as in August 1886 there is a record of Florence Nightingale having telegraphed the superintendent sister at the Deaconess Hospital there to suggest that Catherine visit the Spencer Well's Hospital for Women and Ovariotomy cases in the West End. Later that month Miss Nightingale (pictured) telegraphed Catherine with the following message:

"I sent you Sir Spencer Well's ovariotomy book 'The Revival of Ovariotomy and Its Influence on Modern Surgery, 1884'. The part which concerns us nurses is, I think, more full of the genius of common sense, as far as it goes, than any book I know. I marked a copy for our probationers. I have slightly marked yours chiefly in chapters 7 and 12, but could not mark it all, because I had no time, and besides you do not need it. (The book is a new copy, of which I beg your acceptance, but I was sorry to see a leaf loose, and there was no time to change it.)

Miss Hogg will I am sure, be glad to give you information about men's wards, but I was trying to think of some sister of a female ward who would give you information about ovariotomy, and think that you had better go to Sir Spencer Well's hospital (New Hospital for Women, Euston Rd.)
God bless you. You have my best wishes for your success.

Ever sincerely yours
Florence Nightingale"

There is evidence of Catherine having also travelled to London at least on one other occasion during her time in Newcastle, indicating that not only was she proactive in furthering clinical developments impacting on her role as Matron, but was also sympathetic to the call for nurses to have a system of registration. In June 1888 she attended a meeting of the General Council of the British Nurses' Association, chaired by the HRH Princess Christian, Queen Victoria's third daughter Helena and the Association's first president. The British Nurses' Association had been the established the previous year *"to unite all British Nurses in membership of a recognized profession and to provide for their registration on terms, satisfactory to physicians and surgeons, as evidence of their having received systematic training".*

The British Nurses' Association

In 1884 the British Hospitals' Association[2] had been founded by Sir Henry Burdett, a financier and philanthropist, and under its auspices a Matron's Committee had been established. Within the Association there were calls for a register of trained nurses such as had been introduced in 1858 for the medical profession. The Matron's Committee agreed with registration but argued for three years' training as opposed to the one year supported by the Association.

In 1887, the Hospitals' Association over-ruled the matrons and established a non-statutory voluntary register of trained nurses known as the Burdett Register. Those eligible had to show that they had worked for at least one year in a hospital or infirmary and had undertaken some training in the duties of a nurse.

This resulted in a split in the Matron's Committee between those who supported the Hospitals' Association and those, led by the former Matron of St Bartholomew's Hospital, Ethel Gordon Fenwick (nee Manson)[3], who opposed the new register and sought to align themselves more closely with the medical profession; hence the founding of the British Nurses' Association. Florence Nightingale supported neither group being opposed to any form of regulation for nursing, believing that the essential qualities of nurse could not be taught, examined, or regulated as this would destroy the vocational spirit of nursing.

By the time of Catherine's arrival in Newcastle, overcrowding in the Infirmary had once again become a major issue as Table 15 demonstrates:

	1876	1884	% Increase
In-patients	1630	2578	58
Operations performed	297	908	205

Table 15. Comparison of in-patient numbers and operations performed, 1876 & 1884

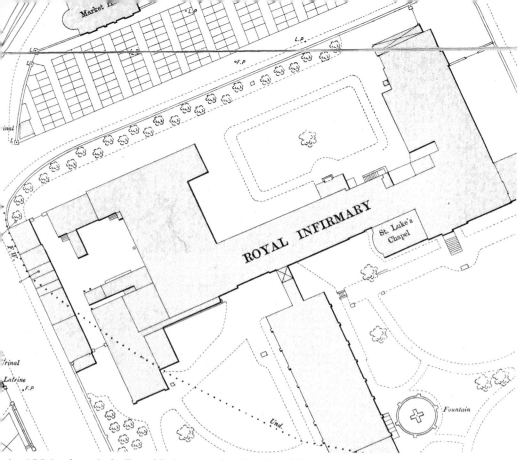

An 1896 plan of the Royal Infirmary showing the addition of the Ravensworth Wing, with the Cattle Market at the rear

The Cattle Market, showing the Market Keeper's house which still stands in what is now Times Square

These increases were a consequence, at least in part, of a reduction in morbidity as surgical techniques had been improved and perfected following the introduction of antiseptic measures. In response a committee was established under the chairmanship of Lord Ravensworth to consider options for increasing the capacity of the Infirmary.

The decision in early 1885, and pending the provision of a new hospital, was to provide 50 beds in a new temporary extension as an off-shoot from the centre of the main block. The Ravensworth Wards, intended to last for five years, were opened in October of that same year, increasing the Infirmary's capacity to 270 beds.

The Ravensworth wing

It would however be more than 20 years before a new hospital was built. The new wards provided accommodation for male patients, releasing space in the main building for fifteen additional beds for women, three wards for children and some additional accommodation for nurses. This development, of course, increased the demand for more nurses.

The late 1880s witnessed a growing desire to promote the comfort of the nurses, not least to provide them with a sitting room. In addition a Miss Taylor provided two nurses at a time with a fortnight's break in the village of Humshaugh, whilst a Mr Hindmarsh gave Catherine £5 to help enable *"her to send nurses occasionally to some salubrious spot, in the outskirts of the city to spend the evening and have tea"*. Meanwhile in 1888 the General Purposes Committee of the Infirmary had reviewed the training schemes for nurses[4] in twelve hospitals and drew up a scheme for 'The systematic instruction and training of nurses'. Probationers had to be between the ages of 25 and 35 and would, following a three-month trial period, undergo three years training, with lectures relevant to the theory and practice of nursing from the Matron as well as the Honorary and Resident Medical Staff. Examinations would be held at the end of each year, uniform would be provided and they were to be graded and paid as follows in Table 16:

Year	Salary £	Grade
First	12	Probationer
Second	15*	Assistant Nurse
Third	18*	Staff Nurse

*Table 16. Proposed annual salaries and grades of nurses in training 1888. *with an option of an additional £2 per annum*

Meanwhile the Infirmary did from time to time respond to calls from other institutions both within Newcastle and beyond, notably Glasgow and Sheffield to provide, on payment of a fee, placements for shorter periods of training. Such matters were always subject to the approval of the House Committee as were another two issues which generated much discussion between Catherine and the Committee. Unexplained losses in the stock of sheets resulted in the tightening up of regulations regarding the transfer of bed linen between laundry, linen room and the wards to prevent pilfering by non-resident staff. Agreement on the time for wakening patients in the morning so that there was sufficient time for serving breakfasts and ward cleaning before the surgical 'dressers' arrived was a matter which Catherine frequently brought to the attention of the committee as she was aware of the need for 'the dust to settle' before the dressings commenced.

Catherine's term of office was also a time of important changes in the governance and management of the Infirmary. Resolving the problem of pressure on beds had not resolved the problem of increasing financial pressures and, following investigation into the issues by a Special Committee in 1887, major changes were made to the constitution of the charity.

1. Access to the Infirmary's services became free to all in April 1888 with the abolition of the letter system of referral. The latter was deemed financially unsound as the cost per patient far exceeded the contributions received from those governors who made an annual contribution; moreover it was also an obstacle to the prompt admission of urgent and deserving cases. The Sunderland Infirmary had made their hospital free some years previously and was being well supported financially by the workmen of their district.

2. The House Committee and the Medical Board were amalgamated; something that had been recommended in the 1870s to overcome the tensions between the two. In addition the House Committee was strengthened by the election of nine worker governors. Any 'Works' could appoint a Governor for every £10 subscribed, and those subscribing less could join forces with another works to appoint a Governor.

3. The appointment of honorary officers was changed. It had previously depended upon the skill of candidates or their friends in canvassing a large constituency of Governors, rather than any judgement of the candidate's fitness for office. A Selection Committee was established to make appointments solely on the personal and professional merits of the applicants.

4. The resident staff was increased to two house physicians and four house surgeons, all of whom had to be fully qualified medical practitioners. Up until now there had been non-qualified medical clerks and surgical assistants.

There were two main benefits arising from these changes: firstly the abolition of the letter system did not result in the withdrawal of support from subscribers; and secondly, on the basis of the Infirmary being made a free hospital, it was agreed to seek permission from Her Majesty Queen Victoria for the Infirmary to adopt the title Royal. This request was granted: hence from 16 June 1887 the Infirmary was designated "Royal Infirmary". By this time the Infirmary had the benefit of a Post Office telephone, however late in 1888 the Northern Telephone Company offered to install free telephones in the Infirmary providing five of the medical staff agreed to have telephones installed in their own homes at a cost of £7 10s. The offer was accepted!

In November 1888 it was reported that about 60 patients a year were discharged from the Royal Infirmary following an amputation. Mrs Arnison, the wife of the Senior Surgeon, had previously set up a system for lending surgical appliances to these and other patients, however they had limited means and the Infirmary did not have the funds to meet the need. Consequently many of the poor suffered much hardship and had their infirmities aggravated from lack of appliances such as waterbeds, air cushions, hearing trumpets, respirators and inhalers. It was decided at meeting in the Infirmary to form the Newcastle upon Tyne Samaritan Society with the purpose of supplying medical and surgical appliances to the deserving poor. Senior medical staff from the hospitals across Newcastle would serve on the Society's Committee.

The Royal Infirmary 1889 Annual Report recorded that in June 1889 Catherine, "*who had, with great diligence and much loving anxiety, carried on the important duties of Matron of the Hospital resigned her charge. Her interest in the work was not diminished, but the laborious nature of her duties pressed upon her strength, and induced her to seek temporary rest.*" At the time of her resignation, Catherine reported that she would be travelling to New York with her brother and sister in September. She sent a letter to Miss Nightingale advising her that she was withdrawing from the work at the Infirmary on account of the difficulty in maintaining a Christian atmosphere!

By 1891 Catherine had returned to the east end of London and was Superintendent of the Friends East End Mission Home for Lady Workers in Tottenham. Ten years later she was recorded as being a visitor at the Retreat in York and described as "Matron of Hospital". In 1911 she was living with her sister Helen and brother-in-law James Rendal Harriss, a Professor of Theology in Selly Oak Birmingham. Catherine died in her home town of Plymouth in July 1924; she was 80 years of age and left almost £1420 to Margaret Ann, the spinster daughter of her brother Frederick Pryor Balkwill. Margaret Ann was recorded in the 1901 and 1911 censuses as being an officer in the Salvation Army.

Timeline

1884   The Home for Incurables opened on Moor Lodge, Hunter's Moor.

1885   The Eye Infirmary moved to St. Mary's Place

1888   The Fever Hospital closed, but was replaced by the City Hospital for Infectious Diseases in Walkergate

1888   The Fleming Memorial Hospital for Sick Children replaced the hospital in Hanover Square

1888   The W J Sanderson Home for Crippled Children was opened in Whickham, relocating the following year to the Red House, Wallsend Green, before transferring finally in 1897 to Salters Road in Gosforth

1888   Publication of the Nursing Record; this was re-named the British Journal of Nursing in 1902.

---

[1] Appointment of the Superintendent of Nurses: By 1881 the 10-year agreement that Mrs Abbot had made regarding payment of the salary for this post came to an end and with it the responsibility for making such appointments reverted from the Honorary Staff Committee to the House Committee.
[2] The British Hospitals' Association was an earlier version of the NHS Confederation.
[3] Mrs Ethel Bedford Fenwick: See Appendix 2
[4] Review of Nurse Training Schemes: Hospitals in Birmingham, Edinburgh, Glasgow, Liverpool, Leeds, and Manchester, were surveyed along with the following London hospitals: Bart's, Guy's, St Thomas's, the London, University College Hospital and the Westminster.

FRANCES HEMBEROW CLOSE
Superintendent of Nurses and Matron 1889-1891

In July 1889 Frances Hemberow Close, who had excellent testimonials, was elected as a successor to Catherine Balkwill at a special meeting of the House Committee. There had been more than 40 applicants for the post with three of them, all from London, being short-listed for interview. Her salary was £105 per annum with "*board, washing, lodging etc*". The Nursing Record reported that she had been the energetic and popular Matron of the Kensington Infirmary, "*with great credit to herself and much advantage to the Institution*"; she would, it was deemed, be very popular in Newcastle.

Frances was born in Stoke-on-Trent in 1856 to John Theophilus Close and his wife Charlotte (nee Hemberow). Charlotte had been born in Chelsea; her father was described as a 'gentleman' and two of her brothers became civil engineers closely involved in the development of the railways. In the censuses 1851-1871 Frances's father was variously described as a general agent, commission agent, and merchant. The family had live-in domestic servants; and by 1871 Frances was a pupil at a girls' boarding school in Daventry. Both Frances and her younger sister, Kitty Hendie Close, were destined to become nurses and acolytes of Ethel Bedford Fenwick[1], founder of the British Nurses' Association.

In 1890 Kitty was appointed Lady Superintendent to the Children's Hospital Great Ormond Street Hospital, however she was blighted by ill-health and her contract was terminated in 1894.

Frances was, between 1878 and 1879, a probationer at the Brownlow Hill Infirmary, Liverpool and thereafter stayed on as a staff nurse to obtain a certificate on the completion of 3 years' service.

Brownlow Hill Infirmary, Liverpool

The Infirmary was one of the largest workhouse infirmaries in the county catering for 1200 sick paupers. At his own expense, William Rathbone introduced trained nurses into the Infirmary with Agnes Jones, a Nightingale trained nurse, appointed Superintendent in 1865 and bringing with her another 12 trained nurses and seven probationers all from the Nightingale School of Nursing. This was the first workhouse infirmary to provide a training school for nurses. Agnes Jones died from typhus in 1868 aged 35.

During 1882 Frances was one of a small group of carefully selected trained nurses sent under the auspices of the Army Nursing Service[2] to support the military campaign in Egypt. She was one of six nursing sisters stationed at the Base Hospital in Ismailia working under Superintendent Sister Caulfield, who was also Superintendent of the Herbert Military Hospital in Woolwich.

In her capacity as Superintendent of the Herbert, Miss Caulfield insisted on having nurses already trained in civilian hospitals and in the need for army nursing sisters to be *"superior educated persons that they might command the respect of the soldier"*.

In recognition of her services during this campaign, Frances was one of seventeen nurse recipients of the silver Egypt Medal, the first British campaign medal to be awarded to women. She was also awarded the Khedive's Bronze Star, a campaign medal established by Khedive Tewfik Pasha a supporter of the British government, to reward those who had participated in the military campaigns in Egypt and Sudan between 1882 and 1891.

On her return in 1883 Frances gained experience at the London Fever Hospital and in 1894 at the Children's Hospital Pendlebury, Manchester. Her next stop was the Monsall Fever Hospital, also in Manchester, firstly as Night Superintendent, and subsequently as Lady Superintendent. In 1887 Frances obtained the post of Matron at another workhouse infirmary, St. Mary Abbott's Kensington Infirmary. Frances was an innovator.

Whilst working at the Monsall Fever Hospital she and the medical superintendent had organised a two year training programme for probationer nurses. In October 1888 Frances gained the London Obstetrical Society Diploma[3] and went on to offer a three months' course of instruction in midwifery at the Kensington Infirmary with places for four trained nurses each year. Prior to taking up her post in Newcastle she had provided a course on Home Nursing for a local Girls' Friendly Society.

Between the years 1888 and 1895, Frances was mentioned on several occasions in the journal the 'Nursing Record'. In 1888 she was described as one of the *"earnest and highly-cultured gentlewomen"* now found willing to accept the matronship of workhouse infirmaries. That same year it was also noted that Frances hosted a meeting at the Kensington Infirmary to discuss the issue of registration for nurses. It was evident that she was in Ethel Bedford Fenwick's inner circle and an active member of the British Nurses' Association (BNA) attending its General Council Meetings. She was the eleventh nurse to sign up to the Association's professional register established in March 1890. In 1891, by which time the Association had been granted a Royal Charter thus becoming the Royal British Nurses' Association (RNBA), a rather grand fourth birthday celebration of the Association was held in the Princes' Hall in

London at which members were presented with RNBA bronze badges. However, Frances, along with Marion Mackey one of her predecessors at the Infirmary, as members of the Association's Executive Committee both received silver badges.

In November 1889 Frances contracted diphtheria; a child had been admitted to the Infirmary in an asphyxiated condition and a tracheotomy had been instantly performed. The child died the following day, and a post-mortem examination confirmed the cause of death to be diphtheria. A few days later Miss Close succumbed to the disease, and was dangerously ill for ten days; however due to *"the skilful and constant exertions of Dr Philipson and Dr Oliver, and the officers of the House"*, Frances recovered and returned to her home in Ilfracombe for a period of convalescence. George Hare Philipson had been an honorary physician at the Infirmary since 1868, and knighted in 1900 for his services to the Infirmary. It is also worthy of note that in 1888 he had been elected to the BNA; thus there was obviously some support amongst the Infirmary's medical staff for the registration of nurses.

George Hare Philipson

One of the Head Nurses acted up during Frances's absence and was awarded five guineas for her "*meritorious service*". Frances returned to duty in January 1890 and that same month Agnes Ross, another Head Nurse was appointed Night Superintendent. Like those before her Frances had to cope with shortages of nurses. One of the problems was the lack of sufficient suitable accommodation. There was no sitting room and the bedrooms were crowded "*in an objectionable manner*". The prevailing view was that young women from the middle-classes who would train as nurses without payment would not do so under such conditions. Occasionally, nurses had to be hired from elsewhere, and sometimes they could not be obtained at whatever cost. Therefore in 1890 it was decided to rent a house, 20 Wentworth Place in Elswick for £50 a year as a Nurses' Home. This provided a bright and cheerful home for all the night nurses whose health, it was deemed, was promoted by the mile walk, morning and evening, between the Home and the Infirmary. A housekeeper and servant were appointed to the Home, and there was now more adequate accommodation in the Infirmary for the other resident nurses.

Meanwhile the Infirmary had become more proactive in recruiting probationers; in September 1889 the Nursing Record had noted that the Royal Infirmary would provide a good training with plenty of practical experience "*for splendid all-round work is done there*" and that Miss Close would doubtless accept suitable applicants. By this time the small salary for first year probationers had been withdrawn and they now received only board, lodging and uniform.

The Infirmary's Annual Report for 1889 also reported that the Honorary Staff and Committee had been anxious to promote the professional knowledge of the nursing staff and that regular courses of lectures were now given to them by the Honorary Medical Officers with the Matron giving regular instruction on nursing duties. By 1890 the Infirmary had 49 nurses, of which eleven were head nurses and the remainder a mix of assistant and probationer nurses. Dr Philipson remarked in June of that year that nursing in the Infirmary had never been more efficient and in September it was agreed to provide Certificates of Competency for those probationers who had successfully completed three years' training. However by November 1890 Frances faced questions from the House Committee regarding the staff changes which had occurred since her appointment and instigated an enquiry, the outcome of which was that the concerns were unfounded.

Frances resigned in March 1891 on the grounds that it was impossible to fulfil all the duties required of the Matron and Superintendent. In addition to her responsibilities in respect of the nursing staff and attendance at all operations, she was expected to accompany the physicians and surgeons on their ward visits as well as managing the household which included the issuing of linen, surgical stores, and uniforms. She stated that she would have resigned six

Newcastle-upon-Tyne Royal Infirmary.

We, the undersigned, representing the House Committee, and the Honorary

Medical and Surgical Staff of the Newcastle-upon-Tyne Royal Infirmary, hereby Certify

that *Isabel Bates* has undergone a Training of *three years*

in this Institution, and that she is, as has been reported to us by the proper officials, a

competent Nurse.

_____ {Chairman of the House
                          Committee.

_____ Senior Physician.

_____ Senior Surgeon.

Dated *twenty seventh* day of *August* 1896

Nursing certificate, as introduced in 1890

months earlier but wanted to wait for the outcome of the enquiry. Frances's resignation did prompt a review of the duties of the office and she remained in post until her replacement was appointed.

She subsequently became Matron of the Fever Hospital in Dublin from 1892 to 1895, before moving on as Matron to a private Nurses' Home in the same city. In 1898 she had an entry in Burdett's Official Nursing Directory and her address was given as Chudleigh, Devon. At some stage she became a district nurse; working in Leicestershire at the time of the 1901 census and in Bakewell, Derbyshire in 1911 where she died in 1918 aged 61 years. Today Frances is remembered as one of the pioneering nurses of the 19th century with an entry on the Kings College London website.

[1]Ethel Bedford Fenwick: See Appendix 2

[2] The Army Nursing Service had its roots in the post Crimean War period although it took many years to flourish. The first six nurses were employed in Woolwich in 1861 and were joined by six more when the Royal Victoria Hospital, Netley opened two years later. This establishment of 12 nurses remained unchanged until the military campaign in Egypt

[3] The London Obstetrical Society existed from 1858 to 1907 having been established in the aftermath of the Medical Act. The Diploma introduced in 1872, recognised the role of the midwife in supervising normal labour

AGNES ROSS
Superintendent of Nurses and Matron 1891-1895

Agnes Ross was born in 1851 the eldest of six children born to William and Euphemia. William was the Presbyterian Minister of Embleton Chapel in Northumberland, he and his wife having recently moved from Scotland. At the time of the 1871 census Agnes was a governess to a family in Tynemouth and ten years later she was still a "governess (teacher)" to a family in Elswick in Newcastle.

At this time the family's middle daughter Elizabeth was a patient in the Children's Hospital in Clavering Place in Newcastle. Agnes's father died in 1880 and in 1881 her mother, Euphemia, was living in Gateshead with Elizabeth, now an elementary teacher. Meanwhile the other daughter, another Euphemia, and born seven years after Agnes, was a pupil nurse at the Derby Infirmary, but at some point moved to the Royal Infirmary, Liverpool as a probationer. In light of a press report some years later it is probable that Agnes commenced nurse training at the Infirmary in 1883.

Following a review, the duties of the Superintendent of Nurses and Matron it was agreed that:

• Her duties should be strictly confined to the superintendence and training of the nurses; the care of the patients; and direction of the nurses in the performance of their duties in the operating theatre

• She would no longer be required to accompany the physicians and surgeons on their ward visits

• The Assistant Matron relieved the Matron of the house-keeping, but also had to be a competent nurse able to act-up for the Matron in her absence.

The Honorary Physicians and Surgeons were invited to make recommendations regarding the suitability of any of the Head Nurses for the post and unanimously recommended the Night Superintendent, Agnes Ross. She took up post on 6 April having accepted a salary of £60, rising according to merit and an allowance of £10 for a uniform dress. The appointment was reported in the Nursing Record, which noted that Agnes had been on the staff of the Infirmary for eight years; she would therefore have worked under both Eliza Peel and Catherine Balkwill.

Agnes Ross was by this time aged 39 and became a hospital matron some seventeen months after her sister Euphemia, who had held matron's posts since 1885, was appointed Matron of the Western Fever Hospital in Fulham, a post she was to hold for the next 32 years. Prior to this, Euphemia had followed Frances Hemberow Close in 1887 as Matron of the Monsall Fever Hospital in Manchester.

The 1891 Census taken on Sunday 5 April, the day before Agnes took up her new duties, identified Agnes as staying with her mother in Gateshead with Frances Hemberow Close still residing in the Infirmary as "Hospital Superintendent" along with 38 "hospital nurses". Another 11 nurses were residing in the Nurses' Home in Wentworth Place, where Frances's cousin Eliza Jane Hemberow was identified as the Matron, having been previously been employed as a governess. Eliza was to remain in this post for another fourteen years.

Towards the end of Agnes's first year in post she was asked to consider ways in which the numbers of nurses could be reduced as over the previous decade there had been a substantial improvement in the ratio of nurses to patients. The information Agnes presented to the House Committee is summarised in Table 17.

Year	Matron	No of Nurses	Annual Cost £	Average No of In-patients
1881	Mrs Peel	28	n/a	214
1884		28	539	
1885	Miss Balkwill	33	621	
1886		40	713	
1887		41	808	
1888		42	814	
1889	Miss Close	42	704	
1890		46	605	
1891	Miss Ross	52*	596	236

Table 17. Numbers of Nurses with associated costs, 1884 to 1891.
*Of whom 17 were 1st year probationers receiving no salary

On receipt of this information the House Committee agreed that there should be no further reduction in the nursing staff, however in future the first-year probationers would be also be required to pay a fee of £7 7s for their training place. Probationer nurses not only provided cheap labour but were now also another source of income! It was noted in the 1891 Annual Report that the Infirmary required not less than fifty skilled nurses and this number could not be reduced; many of the life-saving operations that were performed were of a perilous nature requiring special attendance of two skilled nurses, one each on day and night duty. Sometimes there were as many as three such cases requiring attention at the same time. It was also noted that some nurses suffered personal sickness, and all of them laboured assiduously, and up to their utmost strength. The same report also noted that Agnes had fulfilled her role "*greatly to the satisfaction of the Committee and the Medical Staff.*" Agnes's annual salary was increased by ten pounds and subsequently in early 1895 it was further increased to one hundred pounds.

The profile of the nursing workforce was also changing dramatically as Table 18 illustrates. It had shifted from a reliance on older widows to single women in their 20's and nursing was now becoming increasingly acceptable as an occupation for respectable young ladies and an alternative to employment as a governess.

	Age in years					Number of Nurses	Single	Married	Widow
	Under 29	30 - 39	40 - 49	50 - 60	60 +				
1841		1	3	2	3	9	Not recorded		
1851		5	1	2	1 (75)	9	5		4
1861	3	3	2		1	9		2	7
1871	2	2	1	3		18	6	3	9
1881	23	3	1		1	28	25	1	2
1891	42	6	1			49	48	1	

Table 18. Profile of the nursing staff 1841 - 1891

Agnes referred all matters relating to staff resignations, discharges and appointments to the House Committee having discussed them in advance with Prof Philipson and Dr Arnison. In 1892, this included a proposal for the appointment of a Head Nurse for the operating theatre to take care of the instruments, sponges and lotions, which was approved.

At this time patients were allowed visitors between 2 pm and 4 pm on Tuesdays and Saturdays but only for an hour on Sunday afternoons, and the Rules were also modified following the admission of a an infant aged only one month to allow mothers to be admitted with their young children. The Infirmary was also still advertising for donations of old linen and calico.

In July 1894 Agnes, along with her sister Euphemia, attended the inaugural meeting of the Matrons' Council held in the Great Hall of St Bartholomew's Hospital in London. It had been convened by Isla Stewart, Matron of St Bartholomew's, and was well attended by Matrons from London and the provinces with other letters of support having been received from as far afield as Scotland and Ireland. In summary the objectives of the Council included to:

•   Allow Hospital Matrons to take counsel together on matters affecting their profession

•   Bring about a uniform system of education, examination and certification of nurses in British Hospitals

•   Form an Advisory Committee to which members could apply for counsel in cases of professional difficulty

•   Hold meetings to discuss matters of professional, and general interest

•   Encourage Hospital Matrons to understand the methods of procedure at meetings.

Isla Stewart was elected chairman, and the three vice-chairman included Ethel Bedford Fenwick[1]; Euphemia Ross was one of sixteen elected to the Executive Committee. Many years later, in 1920, Euphemia was elected Vice-President of the Matrons' Council.

Later in 1894 the results of a survey of Nurse Training Schools from across the UK was published in the Nursing Record. At that time the length of nurse training varied between hospitals from one to four years, with some hospitals taking both probationers and paying "lady" probationers. The entry for the Royal Infirmary stated that the age of entry for probationers was 25 to 30. A certificate was awarded for successful completion of three years' training; no salary was given for the first year, but £10 and £15 were paid in respect of the second and third years of training. Depending upon the level of seniority between 14 and 21 days annual leave was granted.

The influential Ethel Bedford Fenwick, as editor of the Nursing Record and a driving force within the RBNA, was in favour of a universal standard of three years' nurse training, and was dismissive of those institutions, including the Nightingale School at St Thomas's Hospital, which continued to provide only one year of training. She considered that nurses must be clean, truthful, healthy, strong and of good temper, and able to prove that they have a good education. As probationers they should receive instruction in theory and practice relating to the principles of hygiene, physiology, anatomy, invalid cookery, and ward and household management.

Late in 1894 it was noted that in a review of another fifteen hospitals, the Infirmary compared favourably in respect of the nurses' working hours, however it was agreed to increase the dinner break from 30 to 45 minutes. The House Committee also conveyed their appreciation to the nurses for decorating the wards at Christmas and for their Christmas entertainment. Early in July the following year, Agnes took the case of Nurse Annie, who had been

NURSES' TIME TABLE.

HEAD NURSES.

RISE,	BREAKFAST,	WARDS,	DINNER,	WARDS,	TEA,	OFF DUTY,	SUPPER,	BED,
7 a.m.	7·45 a.m.	8 a.m.	1·30 p.m 45 mins. allowed.	2·15 p.m.	4 to 4·30 p.m. 30 mins. allowed.	alternate days, 5 p.m.	9·15 p.m.	10 p.m.

ASSISTANT NURSES ON DAY DUTY.

RISE,	BREAKFAST,	WARDS,	DINNER,	WARDS,	TEA,	OFF DUTY,	SUPPER,	BED,
6 a.m.	6·30 a.m.	7 a.m.	12 and 1·30 p.m 45 mins. allowed.	12·45 & 2·15 p.m.	3·30 and 4 p.m. 30 mins. allowed.	alternate days, 5 p.m.	9 p.m.	10 p.m.

ASSISTANT NURSES ON NIGHT DUTY.

RISE,	DINNER,	WARDS,	TEA,	OFF DUTY,	BREAKFAST,	OFF DUTY,	LUNCH,	BED,
7·30 p.m.	8 p.m.	9 p.m.	30 mins. allowed.	8·30 a.m.	9 a.m.	9·30 a.m.	12.	12·30 p.m.

PROBATIONERS.

RISE,	BREAKFAST,	WARDS,	DINNER,	WARDS,	TEA,	OFF DUTY,	SUPPER,	BED,
6 a.m.	6·30 a.m.	7 a.m.	12. 45 mins. allowed.	12·45 p.m.	3·30 p.m. 30 mins. allowed.	alternate days, 5 p.m.	9 p.m.	10 p.m.

SUNDAY.—Nurses who are on duty all day are allowed two hours off.

The Annual Holiday of the Nurses to be three weeks, at such periods as may suit the convenience of the Matron.

The above Rules to be STRICTLY ADHERED TO, except when the Matron finds the arrangements of the Hospital will not admit it

Nurses timetable introduced in 1894

in post since 1878 but was now ill, to the House Committee, which agreed to pay her £5 and arrange for her to be admitted to the Home for the Incurables.

At 9am on Monday 22 July 1895, Agnes aged 43 years, was found dying in her room by the Assistant Matron, Margaret Cash[2] who had responded to the Matron's bell. Agnes was conscious at this time and informed Margaret that she had taken "morphia and lotion" at about 3am that morning and, pointing to the door, reported that she was "sick". Margaret, in spite of Agnes's protestations not to, summoned Dr Beattie, the senior house physician, and he attempted artificial respiration for 20 minutes, unfortunately Agnes died at 9.30am. Dr Beattie subsequently found an empty bottle, which would have contained three ounces of laudanum (tincture of opium), in Agnes's room.

Agnes's death and inquest, held the following day, were reported widely in the local press as well as in the Nursing Record. Margaret Cash reported at the inquest that Agnes had, over the previous few days, been worried and anxious about certain changes that were likely to be made in the Infirmary. Margaret did not know why it should have been such a concern and there was no evidence of any other reason in Agnes's personal life that could account for her suicide. The coroner agreed that the only thing that seemed to account

*Margaret Cash, Assistant
Matron (front left)*

for Agnes's action was the small matter of some unhappiness in respect to some changes that were taking place in the Infirmary. The jury returned a verdict that Agnes had poisoned herself while in a despondent state of mind.

The only 'changes' recorded in the House Committee minutes relate to Agnes's proposals for the replacement of Margaret Cash as Head Nurse on the Ravensworth Ward; Margaret, one of 47 applicants for the post, had been promoted to Assistant Matron the previous month replacing Theordora Pressland[3] appointed in 1890.

On Thursday 11 July Agnes had submitted her recommendations to the Weekly Committee which involved the moving of three or four nurses. The proposals had the support of the medical members of the Committee however three members requested that Matron be asked to reconsider her recommendations on the basis that there were longer serving nurses in post than those she proposed for promotion. Agnes's recommendations were therefore only approved in part with any further decision deferred until the next meeting. The following week on 18 July the decision were referred to the next full meeting of the House Committee. This may or may not have been a factor in Agnes's suicide; however at the Weekly Committee held on the day of Agnes's funeral, the Chairman reported that it was his duty to enter his protest against the practice of some of the Governors spending considerable time in the hospital questioning nurses and others. This undermined the authority of the Head Officers and caused extra worry and annoyance over and above that which was inseparable from the positions held by the Heads of the House. These comments were supported by the medical members of the Committee who strongly condemned the practice as subversive, and did much to harm the harmonious working of the Institution. The following statement is recorded in the minutes:

"The House Committee of the Royal Infirmary, Newcastle-on-Tyne desire to place on the record of their minutes an expression of their sense of the loss they have sustained by the lamented death of Miss Agnes Ross the Superintendent of Nurses and Matron of the Institution. Miss Ross, during the twelve years she was associated with the institution in the various positions she occupied in the Nursing Department always had the esteem and respect of the Committee. She also enjoyed the confidence of the Honorary Medical and Surgical Staff. She was held in highest regard by the nurses and had endeared herself to them by her thoughtful consideration for their comfort and welfare. The Committee feel that she will be much lamented and that her memory will be warmly cherished."

It was reported in the press that Agnes

"had served the Infirmary for twelve years and has gone through every grade of service in the Institution. Her death has thrown quite a gloom over the Institution, and she is deeply mourned by the medical and nursing staff with whom she was very popular and beloved. Her strict attention to her various duties and her ability had won for her the good opinions of all".

Agnes's funeral service was conducted in the Infirmary's chapel by the chaplain. That same day her remains were taken by train from Newcastle Central Station to Chatton Station, accompanied by family and friends, including 17 nurses as well as servants from the Infirmary, she was taken to Embleton where her parents had been buried. However, as a suicide, Agnes could not be buried in the parish churchyard and was interred in the unconsecrated area of Spitalford Cemetery, with her grave simply marked by a small cross inscribed with her name. The burial service was conducted by three local ministers.

Pending the appointment of a replacement for Agnes, Margaret Cash acted-up and she was one of three of the 52 applicants for the post who was interviewed. Two members of the House Committee were in favour of appointing her on a twelve-month trial. Although not appointed, her annual salary was increased from £30 to £40.

Not long after Agnes's death an invitation was received from the Trevelyan's of Wallington Hall offering to entertain those nurses who could be spared; ten nurses were released for a day.

Postscript: Agnes's sister Euphemia had a very successful nursing career which was the subject of numerous reports in The Nursing Record, including this on her retirement in 1921 from the Western Fever Hospital, Fulham: *"Miss Ross had the true spirit of the pioneer, and was an early and enthusiastic member of the RBNA and the Matron's Council. She possessed those somewhat rare gifts of seeing straight and sticking to her principles though thick and thin. She had been a keen registrationist for thirty years, and she never wavered in her personal and financial support during all the vicissitudes though which the movement had struggled to victory. We are glad success came whilst she was in office; and all her old "chums" who have the keenest respect for her integrity, and affection for her generous personality, will wish her years of great happiness in her retirement from active service in the profession she has adorned and helped to consolidate."*

Today Euphemia is remembered as one of the pioneering nurses of the 19th century with an entry on the Kings College London website.

Timeline

1893   Dr & Mrs Bedford Fenwick took over the Nursing Record, which Ethel Bedford Fenwick continued to edit. In 1902 it became the British Journal of Nursing

1895   The Newcastle Dental Hospital and School was founded in 1895 in Nelson Street, moving to premises in the Handyside Arcade in 1906. It subsequently moved to new purpose-built accommodation on the RVI site in 1932, before moving to the old Medical School on Northumberland Road in 1948. Since 1978 it has been located close to the RVI on Richardson Road.

---

[1] Ethel Bedford Fenwick: See Appendix 2

[2] Margaret Cash, entered the Royal Infirmary as a Probationer Nurse in the year 1883, and this was about the same time that Agnes Ross commenced service in the Infirmary. Prior to becoming Assistant Matron, a position that she held until her retirement in 1906, she had been for several years a Ward Sister on Ravensworth Ward. Upon her retirement the Committee placed on record their appreciation of her devoted services as a member of the Nursing Staff. Her death was reported in the 1931 Infirmary's Annual Report.

[3] Theodora Pressland, a member of the British Nurses' Association, was appointed in May 1890 as Home Sister and general assistant to the Matron at the Newcastle Royal Infirmary. She had trained at the London Fever Hospital, Islington, where she remained for three years, earning great credit for the manner in which she passed through her time there. Subsequently, she undertook general training at the Cardiff Infirmary. She resigned her position in the Infirmary to become a part proprietor of a private hospital in Newcastle. Subsequently, in late 1897, she was appointed Matron of the County Hospital in Durham. From there she went on in 1902 to become Matron of Clayton Hospital & Wakefield General Dispensary. She died in Wakefield in 1921

EMILY ASTON
Superintendent of Nurses & Matron 1895-1906

Emily Aston was appointed Matron of the Royal Infirmary, on 7 November 1895, on a salary of £100. Her appointment was announced in the Nursing Record, which noted that she would bring twenty years of varied experience to the post, and would be able to take a leading part in the organisation of the local branch of the Royal British Nurses' Association, recently established in Newcastle.

*Emily
Aston*

Emily was born about 1850 in Aldgate London; she was the youngest of four daughters born to Henry and Maria Aston. Her father was variously described as a ship owner, a grocer, and a retired warehouseman. Her three sisters all married: Maria Margaret to a master mariner, Matilda to a medical practitioner, and Jane to a widowed solicitor.

In July 1875, at the age of 25, Emily entered the Nightingale Training School, as a paying probationer; the legendary Mrs Wardroper was still the Matron of St Thomas's at that time and Miss Crossland was the Home Sister. Emily's record described a remarkable and well educated woman; her moral character was beyond reproach; and she was a thoroughly practical and clever nurse. She showed great tact and judgement and had the potiential to be a good teacher.

On completion of her year's training Emily had hoped to take up a post in Canada; in 1875 the former Home Sister of the Nightingale School, Maria Machin, had taken four nurses out to the Montreal General Hospital but now needed replacements. Emily's plans were put on hold when the opportunity arose for her to work under the superintendence of Emmeline Stains, a nursing sister with whom she had worked as a probationer. The planned move was to the newly established Herbert (General) Military Hospital in Woolwich, which was replacing the old Garrison Hospital. Pending this move Emily was retained by the Training School, along with Emmeline and another two 'Nightingales': Elizabeth Enderby, and Elizabeth Shillington. However, Florence Nightingale wanted the precedent that had been established in the 1868 Regulations for the Military Hospital in Netley to be upheld, and the Superintendent of Nursing to be directly responsible to the Secretary of State at the War Office. This resulted in lengthy negotiations with the War Office which meanwhile had undertaken a restructuring of the Army with the introduction of a linear chain of command. The War Office was adamant that the Superintendent of Nurses must be subordinate to the Principal Medical Officer[1].

By April 1877, the frustrated nurses declined to have anything more to do with the Herbert and consequently Emily stayed on at St Thomas's Hospital. She served firstly as Sister on the Alexandra Ward, a women's surgical ward of 20 beds, followed by six months in 1881 as Sister Superintendent of the Paying Wards on a salary of £60 plus uniform dress, full board, furnished apartments with *"attendance and laundry"*. Emily resigned this post in June 1881 to take up the post of Assistant Superintendent at the Royal Liverpool Infirmary where Emmeline Stains had recently been appointed Lady Superintendent and Superintendent of the Nurse Training School. Elizabeth Enderby moved from St Mary's Paddington to join her former colleagues in Liverpool as Night Superintendent before being selected from a list of 73 applicants to take up the post of Matron at the Cumberland Infirmary in

Carlisle. She held this post from the end of 1882, until she resigned early in 1885 following the death of her cousin General Gordon in Khartoum.

These were the days when the world of hospital nurses was a small one, with the Liverpool hospitals being two of the earliest institutions to be colonised by Nightingales. During the early 1880s Euphemia, sister of Emily's predecessor, the former Matron Agnes Ross, was also nursing at the Royal Liverpool Infirmary, whilst Frances Hemberow Close was nearby at the Brownlow Hill Infirmary, Liverpool. Emmeline Stains died in 1892 whilst still in post at the Liverpool Royal Infirmary and Emily, along with Florence Nightingale, was amongst those who sent wreaths to her funeral.

Memories of Life as a Probationer at St Thomas's

Miss Isla Stewart entered the Nightingale School in 1879 and, following nine months as a probationer, replaced Emily Aston as Sister of Alexandra Ward. Many years later Isla remarked that she was ill-equipped for the post with only nine months' experience. *"After I had been a Sister for a couple of years I realised how much I had learned as a Sister at the expense of the patients. I do not like to remember how much my inexperience must have cost them"*.

Regarding her time as a probationer at St Thomas' Isla recorded that the ward sister and staff nurse were responsible for training the two or three probationers assigned to their ward. Probationers also received lectures in medical and surgical nursing as well basic chemistry and, at the end of the year, were examined on these subjects and their practical work.

The Nightingale probationers lived under the rule of the Home Sister and the Matron. Isla recalled how Mrs Wardroper struck terror into the hearts of probationers, *"she had a firm belief in the wickedness which lies at the heart of all probationers"*. She remembered the Home Sister as *"narrow-minded and hard"*. Isla subsequently replaced Mrs Ethel Bedford Fenwick[2] as Matron at St. Bartholomew's Hospital in London.

Subsequently Emily went on to hold a number of posts both in England and abroad, namely:
• **Superintendent of Nurses at the Government Civil Hospital Ceylon** from June 1884 to April 1886: She wrote to Mrs Wardroper:
"I am feeling much more hopeful about things in general. I believe by slow degrees I shall be able to improve matters. I find the nurses have a great reverence for Miss Nightingale – any mention of her seems to rouse them from their usual apathy. I think perhaps someday Miss Nightingale may consent to write a few lines which I can read to them."
• **Matron at the Eastern Fever Hospital Homerton, London:** Emily returned to England to take up this post in June 1887. It was a poor law

establishment, comprising a 200 bedded fever hospital and the adjacent 100 bedded smallpox hospital. Emily faced numerous challenges during her time at the Homerton, most notably in respect of the medical staff restricting her role to that of housekeeper and undermining her role as nursing superintendent. The Nightingale Fund, Florence Nightingale and Mrs Wardroper were all drawn in to help arbitrate. Emily resigned this post in February 1890 and in due course an inquiry into alleged maladministration at the Homerton was held, with Emily returning to England in April 1891 from her next posting in Gibraltar to give evidence.

• **Matron of the Colonial Hospital, Gibraltar:** This had been a British military hospital but by the time of Emily's arrival it was a civilian hospital serving the local population. Prior to taking up this appointment in July 1890 Emily had also considered postings in Japan and Hong Kong and had sought the advice of Florence Nightingale regarding these options. Whilst in Gibraltar the senior surgeon of the hospital reportedly praised Emily's mastery of hospital management. Emily stayed in Gibraltar until February 1892 when she indicated that she wished to apply for another colonial position.

• **Lady Superintendent of the Strangers' Hospital, Rio de Janeiro:** This hospital served naval personnel passing through the port of Rio and was supported by subscriptions from their shipping companies. At the time of Emily's arrival in September 1893, Rio was under bombardment from mutineer Brazilian gun boats and the hospital (within the fort) was within the range of shells. She wrote to a friend that there were three British gun boats in the bay, but that it was a lovely place *"quite as beautiful as Ceylon but without the languor of the East … the view from the hospital windows is beyond belief"*. In Rio Emily had the support of the 'household staff' and initially a team of six sisters, but they were eventually reduced to two; two having resigned, one to get married; another died; and one returned to England on health grounds. During the first six months of 1894, of the 172 patients admitted there were 149 cases of yellow fever, of which 40 died. The vast majority, 112, were admitted from ships in port. Most of the patients were British with smaller numbers coming from elsewhere in Europe and America. Emily, along with three of her nurses, contracted yellow fever during this epidemic and one of the nurses died. It was whilst she was in Rio in February 1894 that Emily was enrolled on the Register of the Royal British Nurses' Association, and it was this Association which undertook the task of finding replacement nursing sisters. Less than a year later, in May 1895, Emily would complete her term of office in Rio.

In November, Emily was one of five candidates selected from amongst 52 applicants for interview at the Infirmary, and took up post almost immediately. Early in 1896 she was asked to provide the nurses with distinctive uniforms according to grade and soon afterwards the Rules and Statutes for the Infirmary were once again subject to revision. Whilst these remained very much the same as in 1883 it is worth noting that patients who were deemed fit enough were still expected help with the work of the House.

The main changes that reflect the further development of the Matron's role now related to teaching responsibilities: she was now regularly required to instruct the probationers and nurses "in conjunction with the appointed lecturers" and she was required to instruct the nurses about "sick diets" and especially to render, with accuracy, the prescriptions on the diet cards. It was clearly specified that the Matron, House Governor, and Senior House Physician could not all be out of the Hospital at the same time, however the Matron was allowed one month's leave of absence each year with the option of taking it all at once or dividing it into other periods. The Rules for Nurses at this time gave details of the salaries of the nurses, as shown in Table 19:

	Year	Known as	Salary per annum
Probationers	1st	Probationers	None
	2nd	Assistant Nurses	£10
	3rd	Staff Nurses	£20
Staff Nurses (those having gained their certificate)	1st		£24 to £30, rising to £36

Table 19. The salaries of nursing staff in the Infirmary in 1896

The Head Nurses' annual salaries had been reviewed at Agnes Ross's request in 1892, at which time they were increased to between £28 and £30. By 1896 nurse staffing levels were continuing to increase, Emily having been given approval to recruit ten additional nurses, and the accommodation in Wentworth Place was now proving inadequate. It was therefore vacated and three houses in Ravensworth Terrace (6, 7 and 8) were bought and converted into a Nurses' Home, providing accommodation for thirty nurses. However, the demand for accommodation continued to rise and in 1901 another house was taken in Rye Hill. In addition, the nurses' accommodation in the Infirmary was upgraded and refurbished to provide a day room as well as additional lavatories and bathrooms. Although the accommodation available in 1901 was on three sites as shown in Table 20, apparently on occasions some nurses had to be accommodated in the local Young Women's Christian Association hostel:

Nurses' Homes	Accommodation Provided For
Royal Infirmary	10 Sisters and 12 Staff Nurses
Ravensworth Terrace	28 Day Nurses
94 Rye Hill	1 Night Superintendent and 13 Night Nurses
Total	64

Table 20. Accommodation provided for Nurses in 1901

A Section of John Storey's painting of Newcastle upon Tyne showing the Infirmary and the location of the Nurses Homes in Wentworth Place, Rye Hill and Ravensworth Terrace (Summerhill Grove)

Writing in 1900, Professor Frederick Page reported that in comparison to 1870 the nurses were now neatly dressed; there were more of them and they were in every way superior to those who had then been dignified with a name with which they certainly would not be known in 1900. He commented also that the wards were now bright, neat and clean, with pictures on the walls, pianos and an abundance of flowers. There was now an air of comfort and refinement about the wards which there had not been 30 years ago.

These words of praise perhaps reflect, in part at least, the good taste of Emily, whom a former medical student and resident house surgeon, Maurice Jacobs[3], recalled that she used to be referred as 'Chippy' because her "*sanctum sanctorum*" was rumoured to be filled with Chippendale furniture!

In 1896, the year of Queen Victoria's Diamond Jubilee, it was decided that the building of a new Infirmary would be an appropriate commemoration of the Queen's reign. At a meeting in the Town Hall, in October it was decided to build on the Castle Leazes area of the Town Moor on land given to the Charity by the Corporation and Freemen of Newcastle. Queen Victoria commanded that the new Infirmary should be called the '*Royal Victoria Infirmary for the Counties of Newcastle upon Tyne, Durham and Northumberland*'.

The foundation stone of the new Infirmary was laid on 20 June 1900 by the

Newcastle Ward in the Royal Infirmary c1900

Prince of Wales, and Patron of the Hospital. Reflecting the urgent need to consolidate accommodation for nursing staff on one site, the new Nurses' Home was first to be completed and was officially opened in July 1905, providing accommodation for 100 nurses and having views of the country stretching away to the front.

The Homes in Ravensworth Terrace and Rye Hill were closed and Miss Hemberow, who had been in post as Matron of the Nurses' Home since the days of Wentworth Place, was given three months' notice and Miss Jean Elder was appointed to the post of Nurses' Home Superintendent.

During the last decade of the old and overcrowded Infirmary it had to cope with an escalating workload as shown in Table 21. The reduction in the average length of stay did not reflect a more rapid recovery of the patients but rather the sad necessity of discharging patients prematurely in order to find beds for more pressing cases, a situation that will resonate with those managing hospital services today.

	1896	1905
In-patents Admitted	4043	4633
Average Length of Stay	24.69 days	20.91 days
Operations	2043	3699

Table 21. Comparison of the in-patient workload of the Infirmary, 1896-1905

Of the 3699 operations carried out in the Infirmary during 1905, surgery for strangulated hernia carried the greatest mortality, with 18 out of the 71 patients not recovering. Some other operations carried out more infrequently however carried a higher risk of death, for example: ruptured liver, spleen, and gastric ulcer. Table 22 summarises those operations most commonly carried out in the Infirmary during 1905; the number of deaths associated with these particular operations is also given.

Nature of Operation	Total	Deaths
Abscesses	356	5
Inguinal hernia	252	8*
Appendicitis	250	15
Circumcision	173	-
Enucleation of tubercular glands	169	1
Removal of diseased bone	102	-
Eye operations	102	1
Ulcers and lacerated wounds	89	-
Removal of benign tumours	86	-
Compound fractures and dislocations	76	4
*7 of these were cases of strangulated hernias		

Table 22. The most common reasons for surgery in the Infirmary in 1905

Additional information published in the Hospitals Directory for 1905 reported that the Infirmary had 280 beds with an average occupancy of 266. Visiting was still 2-4 pm on Tuesdays and Saturdays and 2-3 pm on Sundays; and patients were required to provide their own knives, forks, butter, towels and change of linen. By the early years of the new century the Infirmary was staffed by over 70 nurses comprising 10 or 11 Head Nurses/Sisters, up to 42 nurses and about 20 probationers. These were in addition to Emily, her Assistant, Margaret Cash, and a Night Superintendent.

In May 1902 at a meeting of the House Committee it was agreed that a Sub-Committee be appointed to consider an appropriate way to celebrate King Edward VII's Coronation. On 9 August, each of the patients was presented with a commemorative beaker and the Chairman of Committee presented silver St. Cuthbert's Crosses to each of the Infirmary's nurses. The front of each cross was embossed with a crown and inscribed with the initials "E" for Edward, "R" for Rex, and "A" for Alexandra. The reverse side was inscribed "Royal Infirmary Newcastle-on-Tyne" along with the initials of the recipient.

The Royal Victoria Infirmary was opened on the 11 July 1906 by His Majesty King Edward VII, accompanied by Her Majesty Queen Alexandra. The fully furnished and equipped hospital provided accommodation for 400 in-patients

St Cuthbert Cross presented to each of the Infirmary's nurses on the occasion of the Coronation of King Edward VI, 1902 (Courtesy Peter Atkinson)

in twenty wards, as well as five operating theatres, a nurses' home, and chapel. The cost of the building, equipment and furnishings was in the region of £300,000. The statue of Queen Victoria was the gift of Riley Lord, who was knighted for his efforts in getting the Infirmary built. On 15 September services were transferred from the old Infirmary on the Forth Banks to the Royal Victoria Infirmary on the Leazes site. The affection felt for the hospital on the Forth is reflected in a poem written by the afore-mentioned Maurice Jacobs[3] which begins and ends with the following verse:

> *My heart's on the Forth Banks, my heart is not here;*
> *My heart is impaled in the cattle-pens near;*
> *Throbs in accord with the steam-engine's stroke;*
> *And dwells in those walls of solidified smoke.*

Emily Aston submitted her resignation in May 1906 and left office in August 1906 when she was approaching her 56th birthday. At the time of the 1911 census, Emily was living alone near Holywell in Flintshire, and was described as a "retired sick nurse" She died in Ipswich on the 6 August 1914, leaving just under £85; probate was granted to her sister Jane Snead now a widow. The British Journal of Nursing reported her death, referring to her as a well-known Nightingale Nurse who had trained in the seventies when long hours and hard work were the order of the day. Emily is another of the Infirmary Matron's listed on the King's College London website of pioneering nurses.

Matron Aston with Sisters and medical staff c1900

Timeline

1902   Both the Queen Alexandra Imperial Military Nursing Service and the Queen Alexandra Royal Naval Nursing Service were established

1903   The Nursing Record was incorporated into the British Journal of Nursing, with Mrs Bedford Fenwick remaining as Editor

1905   The Nursing Times published for the first time

[1]Military nursing service: When this was established as a corps (The Queen Alexandra Imperial Nursing Service) in 1902 its underlying principles were as those laid down by Florence Nightingale; including the Matron-in-Chief being directly responsible to the War Office.
[2] Ethel Bedford Fenwick: See Appendix 2
[3] Jacobs M, *Reflections of a General Practitioner*, London Johnson 1965. Maurice had been a medical student at the Infirmary and in 1900 was one of the 4 resident house surgeons.

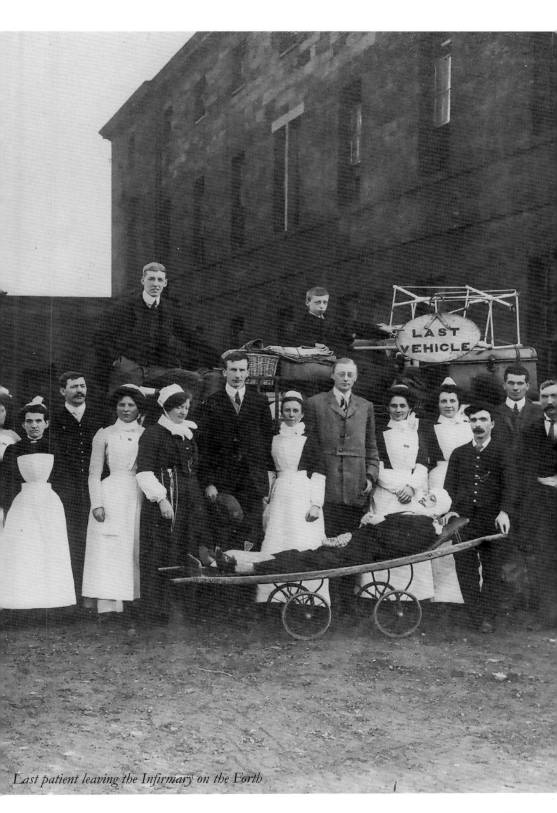

Last patient leaving the Infirmary on the Forth

CHILDREN'S WARD.

IN THE WINTER GARDEN.

THE HALL FROM THE VESTIBULE.

THE HALL FROM THE STAIRS.

THE LIBRARY.

THE BOARD ROOM.

Interior views of the Royal Victoria Infirmary in 1906, featured in the London Illustrated News and declared "a paradise for the sick"

K EDITH McCALL ANDERSON
Lady Superintendent of Nurses 1906-1907

Katherine Edith McCall Anderson was born in 1866, the eldest daughter of Thomas and his wife Margaret. Her father was Glasgow University's first Professor of Clinical Medicine, becoming Dean of the Faculty of Medicine in 1900. He was knighted in 1905 and was appointed Scotland's Honorary Physician to King Edward VII in 1907.

Edith McCall Anderson, courtesy of the Royal College of Nursing

Edith undertook nurse training from 1897 to 1900 at the Royal Infirmary, Dundee. She went on to work with distinction in military hospitals in South Africa during the Boer War for which she was awarded the Royal Red Cross[1]. She worked as a Sister at St. George's Hospital, Hyde Park Corner, then in December 1903 she was promoted to Assistant Matron, a position she held for four years, during which time she had undertaken Matron's duties owing to the illness of the incumbent.

Edith was appointed to the Infirmary on 14 June 1906 on a salary of £150; this was before Emily Aston's retirement, but given the impending move of services from the Forth Banks to the Leazes this overlap would have assisted with the major transition.

The designation of the wards in the sixteen wards in the RVI is given in Table 23. It will be noted that some retained the names of those in the old Infirmary, whilst some new names were introduced.

Edith's stay at the Royal Victoria Infirmary was to be rather brief and by the end of 1907 she had been head-hunted and returned as Matron to St. George's. Still she left her mark at the RVI. W. E. Hume recorded in 'The Infirmary Newcastle upon Tyne 1751-1951 – a brief sketch', that in 1906 the nursing staff had to be augmented and the new Matron had raised the standard of nursing throughout the Infirmary and attracted the best type of probationer. She also was in post to oversee the first two presentations of the Annual Heath Awards for nursing staff.

At the Heath Awards Ceremony in November 1907, the Chairman of the RVI's House Committee, Lord Armstrong, and the Vice-Chairman, Sir George Hare Philipson, both expressed great regret at the impending departure of Edith, who had rendered magnificent service to the institution at a time when zeal, energy, and intelligence were especially necessary in organising "their great Infirmary" in the new premises.

The year following Edith's return to St George's she was appointed to an Advisory Council established by the Army regarding the formation of a Nursing Service for the General Hospitals of the Territorial Force. Throughout the remainder of her time at St George's Edith was actively involved in the Nursing Service of the Territorial Force, as well as with the Nurses' Branch of the Joint War Committee of the Order of St John of Jerusalem and the British Red Cross Society. Edith remained at St George's until June 1914, when she was appointed Matron to the 480 bed Lady Hardinge Hospital at Brockenhurst for wounded Indian soldiers.

The hospital was supported by the Indian Soldiers' Fund, under the auspices of the Order of St. John of Jerusalem. Later in the war she became Matron

Ward		Name	Specialty	Comments
1		King Edward	Male Surgical	
2		Queen Alexandra	Female Surgical	
3	Male	Gibson	Ophthalmic & Aural	Thomas G Gibson JP, benefactor
3	Female	Heath		Professor G Y Heath, Surgeon
4		Northumberland	Female Surgical	
5		Riley Lord	Male Surgical	Sir Riley Lord JP, Mayor of Newcastle and Governor of the Infirmary
6		Hume	Male Surgical	George Halliburton Hume, Surgeon
7		Workmen's Memorial	Male Surgical	
8	Male	Victoria	Children's Surgical	
8	Female	John Ochiltree		His wife endowed beds in John's memory
9		Philipson	Male Medical	Sit George Hare Philipson, Physician
10		Durham	Female Medical	
11	North	J C Eno	Skins	Chemist and benefactor, also brother-in-law of Mary Cooke, Matron 1860-1871
11	South	-	Gynaecological	
12		Ravensworth	Female Medical	
13		John Hall	Male Medical	A ship owner and JP, a benefactor
14		Armstrong	Male Medical	Lord Armstrong, a benefactor
15		Bishop	Male Medical	
16	Male	Percy	Children's Medical	
16	Female	Newcastle		

Table 23. Designation of the wards in the RVI

of the Military Hospital in Nottingham, receiving the bar to the Red Cross. In 1917 Edith's name was added to the Royal College of Nursing's register and in February 1922 to that of the General Nursing Council's register for England and Wales. By 1920 Edith was the general superintendent of the first Helena Residential Club in Lancaster Gate opened for women working or training in London. She died aged 60 in Glasgow in April 1924.

Annual Heath Bequest Awards[2]

In 1905 the Trustees of the Heath Bequest for Nurses in Newcastle upon Tyne announced the establishment of an annual prize-giving for the sisters and nurses of the Infirmary. George Yeoman Heath, Professor of Surgery had given 26 years' service to the Infirmary, and on his death in 1892 he left a generous bequest to the College of Medicine as well as £5000 for the benefit of the Northern Counties Nurses' Home. In 1905 the ownership of the Nurses' Home changed hands and the Charity Commission approved a scheme for the disposal of the interest of this money, which at this time amounted to almost £200 for the benefit of nurses generally in Newcastle.

The Children's Hospital, the Lying-in Hospital, the Infectious Diseases Hospital, and the Union Hospital would each receive £10 for prizes to be awarded to nurses following a competitive examination. Prizes would be awarded annually to the nurses of the RVI, which would be under the direction of the Nursing Staff Committee. Examinations were to be held annually and supervised by members of the honorary Medical and Surgical staff, while the Infirmary's Lady Superintendent of Nurses would report on the conduct and attention to duty of the competing sisters and nurses. The prizes at this time amounting to £52 10s were to be allocated as follows:
5 prizes of £3 each to be awarded to the probationers;
4 prizes of £5 each to be awarded to those top in their final examination with in addition a silver medal awarded for the nurse who came first;
3 prizes for Sisters who would share £17 10s; Marks were allocated as follows:
20% for the general discipline of their ward
20% for the capability and application shown by them in the instruction and training of the probationers under their special charge
60% for a competitive examination in medical and surgical nursing, including invalid cookery.
The scheme was modified from time to time, including from 1908, payment to the RVI of 25% of the premiums of those nurses insured with the Royal National Pension Fund for Nurses'.
The first distribution of the prizes was held in the Library of the RVI on 8 November 1906. Lady Armstrong presented the prizes.

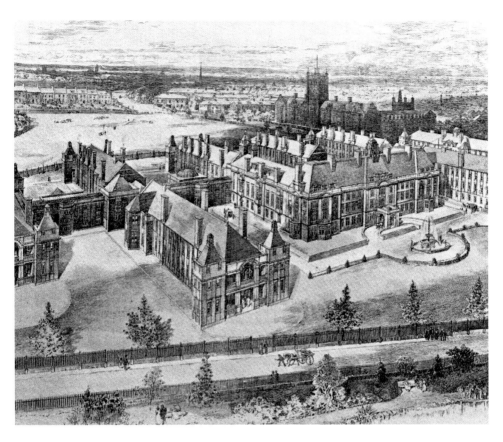

The Royal Victoria Infirmary, 1906

The Heath Medal

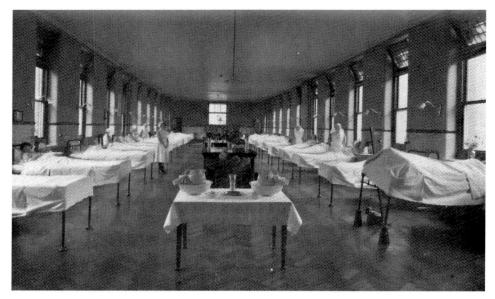

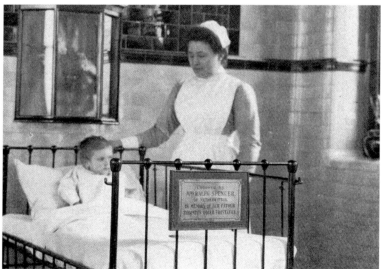

Wards in the Royal Victoria Infirmary

[1]The Royal Red Cross (RRC) was instituted by Queen Victoria in 1883 and was the first British military order solely for women. The decoration can be conferred on anyone, irrespective of rank, who has been recommended for special devotion or competency while engaged on nursing or hospital duties with the navy, army, (and subsequently the air force). Recipients are designated 'members' and can use the letters 'RRC' after their names. The Royal Red Cross, second, class was instituted after the First World War; recipients are called 'associates' and can use the letters 'ARRC' after their names. The badge is almost the same as for the RRC, being silver instead of gold.

[2] Heath Awards: Following a reorganisation of nurse education in 1975 the presentation of prizes was discontinued and for a time a travelling scholarship was endowed. In 1992 the Heath Awards were re-established and from 1996 a Heath medal was also re-introduced.

Lucy Wilson Wamsley, born in 1871, was the second of seven children born to John Maydew Wamsley and his wife Jane. The family lived in Haslingden in Lancashire where John was a Wesleyan Minister. Lucy trained at the Children's Hospital Birmingham, and under the legendary Miss Eva Lückes[1] at the London Hospital, Whitechapel, gaining a certificate in 1897.

Following time there as Ward Sister on Cotton Ward, Lucy had, by 1901, moved to the Royal Orthopaedic Hospital in Hanover Square, Westminster where she held the position of Matron. Prior to her appointment to the RVI in 1907 she was Matron of the Herman de Stern Convalescent Home in Felixstowe.

During Lucy's term of office at the Infirmary she faced a number of challenges; one, inevitably was the increasing throughput of patients after the move into premises that were not only larger but also more 'fit for purpose'.

Table 24 gives an insight into how the work-load of the hospital expanded during this time, requiring an increase in beds from 400 to 430 by 1909 when the ward balconies, not originally intended to hold beds had to be pressed into service for the open-air treatment of tuberculous patients.

	1905	1906	1907	1911
Admissions	4633	4899	6445	7896
Average Length of Stay (days)	20.91	18.7	18.9	18.9
Operations performed	3699	4044	5678	5583
Operations performed incl Out Patients	-	-	-	8499
New Out-patients (including accidents & casuals)	48467	50252	53719	87633
Total OP Attendances			93244	118945

Table 24. Summary of the increase in the work load of the RVI 1905-1911

The Annual Reports of the time provide some insights into the plight of many of the patients accepted for care. It was reported in 1908 that owing to the unemployment the condition of many patients presenting in the out-patient department was aggravated by inadequate food. There was a suggestion from the Medical Staff that local charitable organisations might consider providing them with letters of recommendation to give to those patients whose treatments would be improved by a more nutritious diet. In 1909 an RVI Garment Guild was founded to supply bed garments for those patients who were too poor to provide their own.

Another challenge for Lucy was the need to further develop the nursing service in order to meet the growing demand for skilled nursing. During the early years of the century the nurse staffing levels in the Infirmary had risen to 76, however the move to the RVI required an increase in these numbers and Table 25 illustrates how the numbers had continued to grow up until 1908 when they became more stable.

Nursing Grades	1906	1907	1908	1912
Matron & Superintendent of Nurses	1	1	1	1
Assistant Matron	1	1	1	1
Housekeeper	1	1	1	1
Assistant Housekeeper	-	-	1	-
Linen Room & Class Teacher (from 1910)	-	-	-	1
Night Sister	1	1	1	1
Sisters	10	16	18	20
Nurses & Probationers	74	103	113	113
Total	**88**	**123**	**136**	**138**

Table 25. RVI's Nurse Staffing Levels 1908-1912

Praise for Lucy came from the Chairman of the House Committee in December 1909 when he congratulated her on the harmony prevailing amongst the nursing staff. The Annual Report for 1908 recorded that lecturers and examiners involved in nurse training were now to be remunerated and that it had been found necessary to introduce some modifications to the training scheme. These changes were as follows:

• The first year of training was to be devoted to ward work and classes given by the Matron and Sisters;

• During the second year the nurse was to attend lectures on general nursing; surgical nursing and anatomy; medical nursing and physiology. At the end of that year examinations were held, and the Heath Prizes awarded;

• In the final year of training the nurse was to attend classes on the instruments, sick room cookery and massage. An examination in sick room cookery would be held and three prizes would be awarded by the Heath Trustees; Mrs Arnison, widow of the Professor of Surgery W C Arnison, was the honorary examiner.

In 1910, Lucy reported that, in order to bring the RVI into line with the other great training schools for nurses and to ensure a supply of suitable candidates, the annual pay scales for probationer nurses had been revised. Nurses in their first year were now to be paid £10, whilst those in second year had an increase from £10 to £14. However the third year salary remained unchanged at £20.

Nurses relaxing in their sitting room in the Nurses' Home c1908

Another significant development in 1910 was the appointment of a designated 'Class Teacher' (she was also responsible for the Linen Room; rules regarding the care of the hospital's bedding had been a key feature of the Matron's responsibilities since 1751).

A former nurse[2] recording memories of her training in the RVI during the time of Lucy's tenure of office remembered:

"The hospital was then a charitable institution run by a Committee. Nurses were chosen from what was then called the "better class". This was necessary, as we had to have private means, or a father at the back of us. We had no pay during the first year and had to provide our own uniform. We had a wonderful Matron, Miss Wamsley. We were all afraid of her without cause and grew to like her very much indeed. She recalled that whilst running along the corridor on an errand to the kitchen she ran into Matron who said in a stern voice 'Nurse you walk gently, a nurse never runs, unless it is a case of haemorrhage or fire'. We trained for 3 years. It was hard labour, but very happy."

Professor of Surgery Rutherford Morrison, writing in the Lancet in 1912, reported that each of the wards in the Infirmary had a sister, one staff nurse and three or four probationers. The four operating theatres were under the supervision of one sister and the theatre in which he worked had an instrument nurse, a sponge nurse and an assistant to help as required. He reported that antiseptics were used for the preparation of instruments, dressings and hands, but in addition he and the staff all wore antiseptic overalls, boots, gloves, sleeves, cap, and mask.

Visitors to the theatre were required to wear sleeveless overalls and masks while the entrance to the theatre was sprinkled with 1 in 1000 corrosive solution to fix any dust on their boots. So far as possible he only operated in a properly equipped hospital because he knew the dangers of operating in patients' homes. The photographs opposite illustrate how operating-theatre protocol changed following the move to the RVI. He expressed appreciation for the assistance of trained nurses in the care of abdominal cases, writing:

"In the after-treatment of abdominal cases nothing counts for so much as a good nurse… Certain nurses have a knack of doing well with abdominal cases, and both patient and surgeon are lucky if they get hold of such a one. To be raised up comfortably and packed up skilfully with pillows at the back and under the knees into a half sitting position for a time, even on the second day, is a great relief to most patients. Rolling over occasionally from the back to one side, then to the other and back again, if it can be done without great trouble, as it can by a skilful nurse, is a change that most patients are grateful for. A little drink, a little well-timed sympathy and encouragement, even perhaps a gentle reproof on occasion, are things certain to make a difference between a happy and an unhappy patient, and I believe that in the majority of serious cases the skilled attentions of an intelligent sympathetic nurse can, and do account for the continuance of life and for escape from death."

Visiting hours remained unchanged from the time of Agnes Ross and as telephones at this time were not widely accessible, in 1914 the Infirmary adopted the system introduced some years previously by the City Hospital for Infectious Diseases and which would continue until the mid-1940s. On admission each child was allocated a number which was given to their parent so that they could check in the local press to see if their child featured on any of the lists which were categorised as:
• Dangerously ill
• Condition much the same
• Slight improvement
• Satisfactory progress
• Others doing well

In addition to the internal challenges of the Infirmary another challenge for Lucy was a national one which came in 1908 with the establishment of the Territorial Force Nursing Service.

Operating Theatre in the Royal Infirmary, 1906

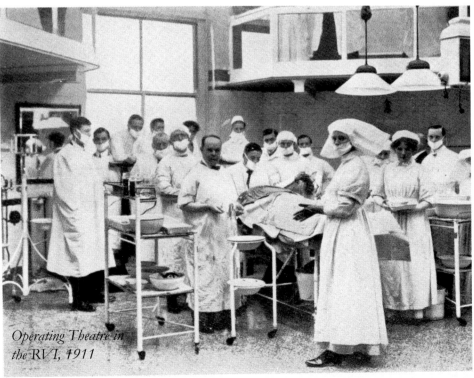

Operating Theatre in the RVI, 1911

Territorial Force Nursing Service (TFNS)

Under the Chairmanship of the Director-General of the Army Medical Service, an Advisory Council was established in connection with the formation of a Nursing Service for the General Hospitals of the Territorial Force. The Territorial Force was a part-time volunteer component of the British Army created in 1908. The remit of the Council was to frame rules for the admission of nurses into the service, and the appointment of Matrons and Sisters along with recommendations regarding the administration of the service.

The sister of the Secretary of State for War, Miss Elisabeth S Haldane, was appointed Vice-Chairman to the Council, along with Sidney Browne[3] RRC as Secretary. Sidney was the first Matron-in-Chief of the Queen Alexandra Imperial Military Nursing Service (QAIMNS), established in 1902, and had concerns regarding the lack of trained nurses available to the Army. It was to this Council that the former Matron of the Infirmary, Edith McCall Anderson, had also been appointed.

Inaugurated in 1908 the TFNS objective was to create 23 Territorial Army General Hospitals in the UK, each with planned accommodation for 520 patients and a reserve staff of 91 nurses who had to be at least 23 years old and had completed three years training in a recognised hospital. These Territorial Force General Hospitals did not have any actual accommodation in peace time; when the need arose they would be housed in public buildings. The civilian nurses who enrolled with the TFNS continued with their normal duties but agreed to be mobilised at short notice in the case of war, and were only required to re-register their intention to serve on the 1 January each year. The Territorial Matrons were required to spend seven days training in a military hospital every second year. Sidney became Matron-in-Chief of the TFNS in 1910.

At the outbreak of the First World War the TF General Hospitals were commissioned, along with 8 territorial hospitals established overseas, the TFNS were mobilised and worked alongside QAIMNS nurses in military hospitals both at home and across the war zones. Up to 8140 nurses served in the TFNS during the war, of which 2280 served overseas.

In 1909 the TFNS was augmented by the affiliation of the Red Cross and the Order of St John which together organised Voluntary Aid Detachments (VADs). Two thirds of these volunteers were women. Female VADs over the age of 23 years, with more than three months' hospital experience were accepted for overseas service. During the four years of war 38,000 VADs worked in hospitals, serving as nurses, ambulance drivers, and cooks.

In March 1909 Lucy was appointed the TFNS Principal and Organising Matron for the district with the founding of the 1st Northern General Hospital (1NGH). It was in this capacity that she was invited in June to witness the presentation of colours of the Force by HM King Edward VII in the grounds of Windsor Castle. Later in 1909 Miss E S Haldane, Vice-Chairman of the Territorial Nursing Service, presented the Heath Awards at the annual prize giving in the Infirmary. She also presented TFNS badges to those RVI nurses who had enrolled with the service. Lucy was congratulated for having secured the services of 110 highly qualified nurses out of the 120 required; of these 28 had trained in the Infirmary.

In 1912 Mrs Ethel Bedford Fenwick[4] spent time in Newcastle and was escorted on a tour of the Infirmary by Lucy. Writing in the British Journal of Nursing, Mrs Fenwick was eloquent in her praise: *"It is beautifully situated and is surrounded by fine well-kept grounds. The approach is stately, and dignity is lent to the whole institution by the well-placed and most lovely statue, in pure white marble, of Queen Victoria"* The inner entrance hall was artistic and beautiful: *"With its stamped leather walls and fine woodwork, the staircase and gallery leading to the Board Room above, give a baronial air"*

Although she considered the polished floors and wooden lockers in the wards as hygienically defective, she did comment they were *"very harmonious"*. The wards she noted had been *"scientifically constructed and beautifully appointed. They are spacious; light airy, and comfortable; and evidently very well cared for"*.

The whole institution was *"speckless"*. She commented on the approach to the Nurses' Home through the lovely winter garden, the corridor and conservatory being *"gay with flowers, ferns and creepers"* and there was approval for the grounds, accessed from the recreation rooms, which were reserved for the nurses. In regard to the Nurses' School, there was she reported, a very high and practical standard of training in force and the probationers were systematically taught and their studies supervised. She was impressed that £18,850 of the previous year's income of £37,985 had come from the contributions of workmen.

The previous year the coronation of H.M. King George V and Queen Mary, on 23 June 1911, had been celebrated in the Infirmary with tea and entertainments provided in all the wards; with souvenirs of the event given to every patient. A brooch was also presented to each maid and a silver St Cuthbert cross was presented to each nurse. This time the crosses were inscribed with the initials "G" for George, "R" for Rex, and "M" for Mary, and the reverse bore the nurse's initials, and Royal Victoria Infirmary, Newcastle upon Tyne.

In October 1912 it was announced that Lucy had been appointed an Inspector under the Local Government Board. The House Committee passed a resolution of thanks to Lucy for the admirable way in which she had carried out her duties during her tenure of office: *"Through her consistent action and kind consideration for the comfort and welfare of the Sisters and Nurses she has enjoyed their confidence and esteem"*. Lucy retired from TFNS in 1913 but was granted permission to retain and wear the badge of the TFNS in recognition of her valuable service.

It is obvious from reports in the nursing press that in her new capacity Lucy's robust reports were not always well received by those inspected. Lucy, however, was eventually promoted to the position of Assistant General Inspector with the Ministry of Health and was awarded the OBE in the 1929 New Year's Honours. Lucy lived for a while in Windermere in Westmorland, before moving to Bexhill in Sussex, where she died in 1947 leaving almost £31,000

Timeline

1907 The Nursing Mirror was published for the first time, ceasing publication in 1985

1910 Death of King Edward VII and accession of King George V who consented to become Patron of the RVI.

1912 Women's suffrage groups paraded through Newcastle and 6000 gathered to listen to speeches on the Town Moor.

1913 The TB Hospital opened as an outpatient clinic in Newbridge Street, Newcastle.

---

[1] Eva Lückes was appointed as Matron of the London Hospital at the age of 26 years in 1880, a post she held for 39 years. Edith Cavell was one of her probationers. She was awarded the CBE in 1917. Florence Nightingale was her mentor and they collaborated against the campaign for the state registration of nurses led by Ethel Bedford Fenwick.

[2] Nurses' League Magazine, 1974: Mrs B M Golding (nee Proctor),

[3] Dame Sidney Browne, GBE, RRC entered nursing in 1878 and had worked as a staff nurse at St Bartholomew's under Ethel Manson (later Mrs Bedford Fenwick) prior to joining the Army Nursing Service in 1883. Following her retirement in 1906 she became an active campaigner for the state registration of nurses. She supported the establishment of the (Royal) College of Nursing and became a member of Council, its first Honorary Treasurer, and Inaugural President.

4 Ethel Bedford Fenwick: See Appendix 2

ESTHER FLORENCE CORSER BROWN RRC
Assistant Matron, 1909 - 1913
Superintendent of Nurses and Matron 1913-1928

Esther Florence Corser Brown was born in Dudley in 1870; she was the third of seven children born to James Brown, a surgeon and his wife Ellen. She trained, 1895-1899, at the Leamington and South Warwickshire Hospital and had been Sister at the Royal Portsmouth Hospital, where she did temporary duty as Assistant Matron. Following time as a private nurse at the Sussex County Hospital, Brighton, she was appointed Assistant Matron at the Cancer Hospital, Fulham Road, subsequently renamed the Royal Marsden Hospital. She is also recorded as having been secretary of the Army and Navy Male Nurses' Association.

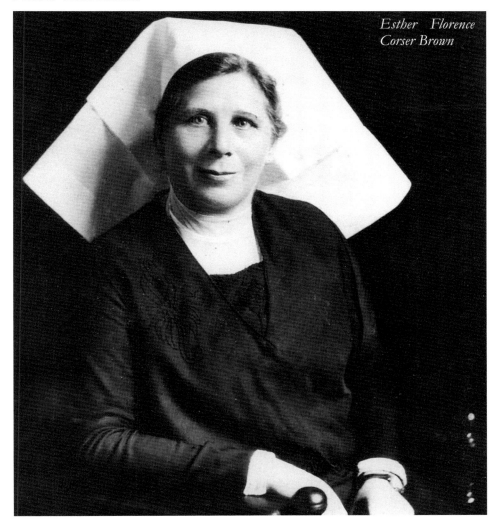

Esther Florence Corser Brown

Resident Staff - Medical in Nu...

Esther had been appointed Housekeeper to the RVI in March 1908 and the following January she was promoted to Assistant Matron. In August 1909 she joined the Territorial Force Nursing Service (TFNS) and was appointed Matron to the 1st Northern General Hospital (1NGH). Following Miss Wamsley's resignation, the Infirmary sought recommendations regarding a suitable replacement from Miss Wamsley, Miss McCall Anderson, Matron Lückes at the London and Mrs Bedford Fenwick. In December 1912 Esther, having been recommended by Lucy Wamsley, was appointed Superintendent of Nurses and Matron to the Infirmary and took up her post in January 1913.

The British of Journal of Nursing reported Miss Brown's appointment, and commenting on the Infirmary's excellent nurse training school noted that its nurses may aspire to the best posts, thus *"naturally encouraging a desirable class of woman to enter the school"*. The report also commented that the training given in the provincial hospitals was *"often practically better than in the metropolitan (London) hospitals where medical students abound"*.

A few months later Miss Brown also replaced Miss Walmsley as Principal Matron of 1NGH and as such was accountable to the Matron-in-Chief of the TFNS, Miss Sidney Browne, who was based in the War Office in London.

Esther's appointment to the Infirmary came at a time when the demand for hospital services in Newcastle was spiralling out of control. The 19 hospitals, plus private hospitals and dispensaries providing a total of 2750 beds in Newcastle were not meeting the needs of the city. Consequently the pressure on beds in the Infirmary, which had been founded to provide care for the sick and lame poor from Newcastle, Northumberland and Durham, and received two thirds of patients from outside of the city, was unremitting.

The House Committee therefore took the decision to provide a further 36 beds in the Infirmary. In order to find accommodation for the increased staff three houses in nearby Leazes Terrace were converted into a Servant's Home, releasing 30 rooms in the Nurses' Home. The need for an increase in income

al Victoria Infirmary, Newcastle on Tyne.

was essential as in addition to the expanding numbers of patients, hospital treatment was now becoming more expensive; surgical techniques were constantly improving, and new diagnostic and therapeutic interventions, such as X-rays, and radium were being introduced. The generous contributions from the workmen of the district was larger than any similar contributions made elsewhere in the UK, but the Infirmary now needed generous support from others. There was, of course, considerable upheaval resulting from the outbreak of war the following year.

The war brought a requirement by the Admiralty and the War Office for the Infirmary to provide 200 beds for the treatment of wounded sailors and soldiers. The response of the Infirmary was to build and equip two new pavilions each containing 26 beds, adjoining wards 5 and 6. In addition the out-patient service was limited to those who required specialist advice, and the out-patient waiting hall was converted into a 42 bed ward.

The Infirmary now had 565 beds of which 200 were devoted to the military for which the War Office made a contribution of 3 shillings per patient per day. In 1917 this contribution was increased by nine pence for each occupied military bed and three pence for each of those unoccupied. During 1918, fifty-six of the 200 military beds were released back into normal service with further beds being made available the following year.

At the outbreak of war 13 of the Infirmary's resident physicians and surgeons enlisted with the Naval and Military forces, increasing the workload of the honorary medical and surgical staff who were now also providing services, including X-ray and pathology to the 1NGH based in the nearby Armstrong College. Fourth and fifth year medical students responded by offering their assistance to the Infirmary. A decision was soon made to recruit resident lady doctors to the Infirmary. By the end of 1915 the Infirmary had treated more than 5000 Naval and Military sick and wounded soldiers, some of whom were introduced to King George V when he visited Wards 5, 5a, 6, and 6a in May. That year Esther's salary was increased from £150 to £200.

The logistics of recruitment and allocation of nurses at this time must have been a continuing challenge for Esther and her small team of assistants.

•   The initial response from the Infirmary's nursing service was robust with nine sisters and six nurses enlisting. By the end of the 1915, 26 members of the nursing staff had left the Infirmary to take up posts with the TFNS or to join Naval or Military hospitals or ships. Two years later, in 1917, another 34 nurses and sisters enlisted, to be followed in 1918 by a further 21.

•   In addition, 90 Territorial Force Nurses of the 1NGH were allocated to the Infirmary; 20 of them being provided with on-site accommodation. In 1915 these nurses were withdrawn and had to be replaced by civilian nurses all of whom, of course, required accommodation.

•   Arrangements were also made for 20 members of the St. John Ambulance Brigade and the British Red Cross – Voluntary Aid Detachments (VADs) - to gain experience in the Infirmary each month.

•   The following year the Infirmary also responded positively to a national appeal for hospitals to admit some probationers for short periods of training during the war, so that they might be available for work later, under supervision in military hospitals. In 1915 Esther was authorised by the House Committee to admit special probationers with the proviso that they could be accommodated in the Infirmary. This was followed by a decision to add a temporary annexe to the Nurses' Home to provide accommodation for 12 nurses and six resident lady doctors.

Meanwhile Esther also had her responsibilities as Principal Matron of 1NGH to fulfil, for which she was awarded the Royal Red Cross Decoration, First Class, which she received from King George V in January 1916 at an investiture at Buckingham Palace.

1st Northern General Hospital 1914-1918

Based in Newcastle this was a designated "Home" based military hospital which, following the outbreak of war, took over the principal buildings of Armstrong College[1] to provide 540 beds for the reception of the war wounded. In 1914 the nursing establishment of 1NGH comprised: one Principal Matron, Esther F C Brown; 14 Sisters; and 28 Staff-Nurses; but following the introduction of VADs there were 14 staff-nurses and 21 VADs. By 1917 the bed complement of 1NGH had risen to 995 beds on split sites including: 141 beds in the Barras Bridge Assembly Rooms; a tent hospital with 200 beds; and a hut with 114 beds. This increased again to provide 104 beds for officers and 1420 for other ranks. In 1918 at the height of demand 1NGH provided 2166 beds.

By 1916 there was growing concern that the war would leave a legacy of thousands of soldiers suffering from maimed limbs and requiring lengthy treatment in properly equipped hospitals. This resulted in the City Council and the Freemen of the City agreeing to transfer another 15 acres of adjacent land on the Leazes site to the Infirmary[2]. An orthopaedic block comprising

25 beds, primarily for orthopaedic military pensioners, was developed on this site in 1917 along with accommodation for the radiological and massage services; the latter facilitating the opening of a Massage School in October 1918. In 1920 the management of the Orthopaedic Hospital was transferred to the Pensions Ministry; however the Infirmary retained the use of those support services provided in the block. Meanwhile the treatment of venereal disease[3] had become a major health priority for the Government and the voluntary hospitals, which would be appropriately funded, were enlisted to help. The Infirmary's scheme to provide 24 beds in a temporary ward, erected between another two of the wards on the ground floor of the Infirmary, was approved and the facility opened in 1917.

In 1918 it was decided to proceed with plans agreed prior to the outbreak of war for extensions to the wards, the Nurses' Home and the provision of new wards, but these would all take time and meanwhile post-war pressures brought an ever increasing demand for services. Waiting lists were lengthening and the premises for both patients and staff were rapidly becoming inadequate to meet the demands placed upon them. In 1919 it was reported that wards initially intended for 24 patients were now at times providing care for up to 45 to 50 patients. Major surgical advances had been made during the war, particularly in respect of orthopaedic and chest surgery; and meanwhile scientific knowledge was expanding with new treatments for an increasing number of conditions, such as diabetes and pernicious anaemia.

Of the 139 patients admitted during 1923 with diabetes mellitus, 86 were treated with insulin, which had first been used to treat diabetes the previous year. In 1928 a voluntary blood transfusion service was introduced into the Infirmary. During the 1920s the Infirmary had become concerned about the increasing number of motor vehicle accidents, and in 1924 the House Committee took the matter to the City Council, hoping that action could be taken to reduce the accidents but also with the object of obtaining more financial support from the Council. As Table 26 illustrates, these numbers continued to grow over the next four years, although the proportion requiring in-patient care had diminished.

	Total number of casualities		
	Treated	Admitted	Died
1925	595	282	33
1928	1301	436	Not known

Table 26. Cases of Motor Vehicle Accidents seen in the RVI 1925 & 1928

By 1919 the provision of convalescent facilities was identified as one way in which to help reduce the pressure in the Infirmary, however it was not until 1923 that the Innes Hopkins Memorial Home in Ryton on Tyne opened, providing facilities for 30 patients. Other measures for increasing capacity were dependent on the vacation of the Castle Leazes site by the Ministry of

Pensions Hospital, when its lease expired in 1928. Meanwhile it was not infrequent, even in 1928, for up to 40 patients to be accommodated on the wards in the Infirmary and Table 27 shows how both the demand for both patient services and the nursing workforce increased during the years of Esther's time in post.

	1913	1928
Total number of nurses	138*	197
Beds available	430	572**
Average number of beds occupied	414.4	600
Maximum number of beds occupied	446	653
Average Length of Stay (days)	18.75	15.1
Admissions	8507	14,469
Out-Patient Attendances	101,736	388,897
Operations performed (In & Out Patients)	8457	15,836
Patients on the Waiting List	1254	1932
* 1912 data ** including 30 beds at the Innes Hopkins		

Table 27. Patient activity and nurse staffing levels 1913-1928

Soon after the war, and pending the planned extension of the Nurses' Home, Cross House in Upper Claremont (Road) was purchased and by 1919 an annex had been added providing accommodation for sixty nurses. In 1913 the Infirmary had a nursing complement of 138; this increased during the war years and growth continued until at the end of Miss Brown's tenure of office in 1928 there were 197 nurses in post, 190 of whom were ward or department based. This number included about 130 probationers who undertook a four-year certificated training programme.

The war had not dampened the campaign for the registration of nurses and in December 1916 the matter was discussed during a visit to the Infirmary of the Chairman of the recently established College of Nursing. In September 1918 Miss Brown was elected chairman and local representative of the newly established Northumberland and Durham local centre of the College of Nursing. Subsequently in June 1919 Miss Brown, presented a paper at its Annual Meeting in Manchester regarding the role of the College's local centres in helping to bring about greater uniformity in nurse training. In April 1924 she addressed the local College of Nursing Centre in Newcastle regarding the attainments to be acquired by a nurse which she summed up as follows:
1) Great skill in nursing the sick and injured;
2) A high standard of knowledge of the laws and functions of the human body;
3) Great skill in 'handling', that is in tactfully managing her patient;

4) A good knowledge of hygiene, also foods and feeding of the sick and invalid cookery;

5) Some knowledge of housekeeping, of the care of linen, and a good knowledge of economy;

6) Power to keep silence over her patients' affairs: *'If thou hast heard a word let it die with thee'*;

7) Great powers of observation

8) She should try and accustom herself cheerfully to go on doing monotonous work for which there is little to show, without getting narrow, discontented or bored.

The (Royal) College of Nursing (RCN)

This was founded in 1916 with 34 members but grew within a year to 2553 and continued to flourish thereafter.

The objects of the College of Nursing were to:
• Organise the nursing profession;
• Secure State Registration for trained nurses;
• Make and maintain a register of trained nurses;
• Promote the interests of trained nurses, and to raise the standard of training;
• Establish a universal curriculum of training, and to establish lectureships, scholarships, and in every way to promote the advancement of the nursing profession.

In 1919 the College's campaign to establish a register for nurses was finally realised with the passing of the Nurses' Act. In 1939 the College was granted a Royal Charter

The Nurses Registration Act of 1919 was an incentive for the establishment of the RVI's Preliminary Training School (PTS) for probationers based in Cross House in 1921. The following spring the Infirmary was included in the list of General Nursing Council (GNC) approved Training Schools. During 1923, 51 probationers entered the PTS and that same year the first Sister Tutor to the Infirmary was appointed. Miss M B Salton[4] trained at the Leeds General Infirmary and held the Leeds University Diploma in Nursing[5]. The examiner for the Heath Awards in 1923 commented that the examination papers had given evidence of careful teaching, and an improved standard of education and practical work. Esther was congratulated on being able to turn out such good nurses, and the following year she was appointed to the GNC Board of Examiners for the General part of the register.

The first GNC Preliminary Examination was also held in 1924 with 25 out of the 32 first year probationers from the RVI reaching the required standard. In 1928 Miss Salton returned to Leeds General Hospital as Assistant Matron and was replaced by Miss U M Sutton from Guy's Hospital.

General Nursing Council for England & Wales

The General Nursing Council (GNC), in conjunction with those in Scotland and Ireland, was founded in 1920 following the Nurses' Registration Act of 1919. Its function was to decide the rules for admission to the register of qualified nurses, which they were to compile and maintain, and to act as the disciplinary authority of the profession. It was also invested with the authority to inspect and approve schools and training courses. The campaign for state registration had been long led by Mrs Ethel Bedford Fenwick[6], whose name appears first on the Register, and later picked up by the College of Nursing. The Council comprised nine lay members and sixteen nurses, 11 of whom were matrons or former matrons, including representatives from the workhouse infirmaries, the Royal British Nurses' Association and from the College of Nursing.

The Register was opened in 1921 and by 1923 there were 12,000 nurses on it. These first nurses were admitted if before 1 November 1919 they had been engaged for three years in bona fida practice and had adequate knowledge and experience of nursing the sick. It was under these criteria that the Matron of the RVI, Miss E F C Brown number 2812, registered on April 21 1922 with her Assistant Matron, Miss A Charteris number 8510, registering on 27 October 1922.

Thereafter nurses were required to pass a final state examination; the first of which was held in 1925. The register distinguished between the various specialties with different parts of the register for general nurses, children's nurses, mental nurses, mental deficiency nurses, fever nurses, and had a supplementary part for male nurses.

Registration however did not become compulsory until 1943. In 1943 the responsibilities of the GNC were extended to include a register for assistant nurses. Male nurses did not join the main nursing register until 1951.

By 1919 the working conditions of the Infirmary's nurses was becoming a matter of closer scrutiny with the day and night nurses working almost 70 and 80 hours a week respectively. There was a proposal to introduce a 48-hour week, and a plan to reduce the nurses' hours when more accommodation became available for the recruitment of additional nurses. Meanwhile the numbers of ward maids were increased to relieve some of the work undertaken by the nurses. By 1923 it was reported at the Annual Court of Governors that there had been a proposal to reduce the working day of the nursing staff to eight hours however as this would incur a cost of £2988, the decision was deferred. It was noted, however, that the average weekly nursing hours had been reduced from 70 to 62 hours! A workman Governor commented that a seven-hour day was considered sufficient for a pit pony.

In spite of the pressures the nurses were working under, they were prepared to go beyond the call of duty and helped with fund-raising for the Infirmary. In November 1921 Esther and the nursing staff held a bazaar raising £1880, £500 of which was invested for the endowment of a cot and the remainder to go into general funds. In 1925 another bazaar was held raising £797 towards the cost of providing two hard tennis courts and equipment for the PTS. By 1926 two tennis courts had been installed in the grounds of the Nurses' Home. However, it was not only nurses who engaged in fundraising. In 1922 it was reported that £500 had been collected during the previous eighteen months by the retriever 'Sweep' which stood at the Infirmary gates.

Matron Brown with the dignitaries at one of the Nurses' Bazaars

Esther retired aged 57 on health grounds in April 1928, having served the Infirmary for 20 years and been Matron for 15 years. She had been supported by three Assitant Matrons, initially from 1913 by Sarah Williams[7], later by Flora J Jones[8] and, from 1921, by Annie Charteris. She had steered the Infirmary's nursing service and the local TFNS, now known as the Territorial Army Nursing Service (TANS), through the tumultuous period of the war, and subsequently the changes consequent on the introduction of state registration for nurses. The House Committee passed a special resolution of thanks for the admirable and efficient manner in which she had carried out her duties during her tenure of office and in recognition of her services agreed to pay her pension. Esther also resigned her post as Principal Matron of 1NGH. The Secretary to the Territorial Army Association in Northumberland recorded the Association's appreciation of the service that Esther had given, commenting on her "*extraordinary powers of organisation, and unfailing tact combined with firmness*". He also noted that she had been most helpful in training members of the VADs.

At the time of the 1939 Register, Esther was living in Dudley with her sister Winifred and her brother Oliver, a retired bank manager. She died in Dawlish, Devon in 1958 aged 87 years, leaving £9727. It was proposed and agreed at the first executive meeting of the RVI Nurses' League that a memorial of some kind be placed in the chapel in her memory.

Timeline

1921 **Banting and Best discovered insulin.**

1923 **Foundation of the Babies Hospital and Mothercraft Centre based on the Day Nursery established in 1917 at 33 West Parade in Newcastle.**

1928 **Sir Alexander Fleming discovered penicillin, but it was not until 1942 that it was first used on humans.**

---

[1] Armstrong College: the University of Durham base in Newcastle of the Colleges of Physical Science and Medicine.

[2] Leazes Site: This site could not be used solely for civil purposes at this time. It was therefore envisaged that the facility would be used for the benefit of injured servicemen and military pensioners, as well as those from the civilian population who had been injured in factories, workshops or mines. In 1928 the hospital was relocated to Dunston Hill in Gateshead, after which the buildings were converted to provide private accommodation for 86 paying patients, as well as an operating theatre, in what became known as the Leazes Hospital.

[3] Venereal diseases were the major medical reason for the hospitalisation of troops during the war. As early as September 1914 the military authorities had taken over the Workhouse buildings, as a specialist venereal disease hospital for officers and men, the male block (100-200 beds), which became known as the Brighton Grove Hospital. Subsequently the number of beds used for this purpose in the rest of the Workhouse as well as the Workhouse Infirmary, increased from between 400 to 500 in January 1915 to over 700 by July. Eventually the Board of Guardians sought compensation for the use of 1000 beds.

[4] Margaret Bessie Salton originated from Hartlepool and became Matron of St Mary's Hospital Paddington in 1933, a post which she held until her death at the age of 44 years.

[5] The Diploma in Nursing, Leeds University was instituted in 1921 and open to nurses who had completed four years' certificated training in a General Hospital recognised by the University. Candidates were required to spend at least three months attending courses approved by the University either in the University of Leeds or the Leeds General Hospital and attend a course of lectures in the University on Social Economics or some other approved subject. Nurses could register as a candidate at any time following acceptance for nurse training and on the production of evidence of general education. The examination could only be taken after receiving a certificate of completion of four years' training and confirmation of attendance at the prescribed course of lectures. The examinations, held twice a year, included written papers, practical work and a viva voce. Fees of 5 guineas were payable to register as well as prior to the exams.

[6] Ethel Bedford Fenwick: see Appendix 2

[7] Sarah Williams, the Assistant Matron and TFNS Matron 1NGH took up the post of Matron at the 2nd Eastern General Hospital, Brighton. Sarah was awarded the RRC in October 1917 and the following month, having volunteered for active service abroad, she was transferred to the 21st General Hospital in Egypt where she served until July 1919. She returned to her post in the Infirmary after the war, but resigned in 1921 to become Matron of a TB hospital in Cheam and subsequently. Sarah returned to Brighton when she was appointed Matron of the Royal Sussex County Hospital.

[8] Flora J Jones trained as a fever nurse at the Brook Fever Hospital prior to further training at the Preston Royal Infirmary, Lancashire 1899-1902. By 1914 she had undertaken duties at the RVI as a housekeeping pupil, holiday sister, and Assistant Matron a post to which she returned in January 1916. She was appointed joint honorary secretary to the Northumberland and Durham local centre of the College of Nursing established in September 1918. In 1923 she was working as a private nurse at a Nursing Home in Granville Road Jesmond, a post she held until at least 1940. She died aged 84 years in Alnwick in 1959.

ANNIE CHARTERIS
Assistant Matron 1921-1928
Matron 1928-1946

Annie Charteris, daughter of Peter and Anne, was born in Sunderland in December 1884; her father was a commercial traveller dealing in drapery. The family had moved to Newcastle by 1891 however by 1898 both of her parents had died and Annie, in her early teens, moved in with her paternal Aunt Jane and two cousins. Jane Turnbull was the widow of a master mariner and lived in Westgate in a six-roomed house. Annie had served three years as a probationer at the Children's Hospital in Gateshead prior to entering the Infirmary as a Probationer Nurse in December 1906.

Annie Charteris

She was promoted to Staff Nurse in June 1909 and Ward Sister in October 1910. In September 1915 she was appointed temporary Night Sister and went on to become Home & Class Sister in August 1918 and Assistant Matron in April 1921. In 1919 the London Gazette published a supplement listing the names of ladies who had been brought to notice for their valuable services in connection with the war; this list included Annie in her capacity as Night Superintendent at the RVI. Annie registered with the General Nursing Council in October 1922 within a year of the Register having opened. In May 1928 she was one of four of the 28 applicants interviewed for the post of Matron, and her appointment was unanimously agreed by the House Committee. Soon after her appointment Sister Mary Batey[1] was appointed Assistant Matron, a post which she held until 1945.

Almost immediately following her appointment Miss Charteris was approved as Esther F C Brown's replacement as Principal Matron of the 1st Northern General Hospital (1NGH). This role was described as not too onerous; the main responsibility was to maintain the Roll of Nurses willing to serve the country in time of need, for which the War Office paid Principal Matrons £25 per year. Although Miss Charteris had not previously been a member of the Territorial Army Nursing Service (TANS) it was noted that she had always been interested in the work and had helped her predecessor at the time of completing the annual nominal Roll of Nurses. In April 1930 she was presented with her TANS badge by Queen Mary in Buckingham Palace and in 1935 received the Silver Jubilee Medal in honour of the 25th Anniversary of the coronation of King George V and Queen Mary.

In 1932 Miss Charteris gained approval to order hospital badges for those nurses who had trained in the Infirmary. This badge is a lasting legacy of Miss Charteris's term of office and has been worn with pride by its recipients ever since.

In 1933 Sister E Murray, who had trained in the RVI and undertaken a Sister Tutor's course, was appointed Sister Tutor in place of Miss Sutton who resigned to take up the post of Assistant Matron-in-Chief of the London County Council. The following year Cross House was disposed of and the Preliminary Training School moved into the now extended Nurses' Home.

Two former probationers[2] recalled their memories of Cross House in the 1973 Nurses' League Magazine. The Sister Tutor and Home Sister were resident in the House and gave lectures. Probationers were accommodated in unheated wooden huts erected in the grounds, although some lucky ones shared an attic on the third floor of the House. In the winter probationers were so cold that they went to bed wearing *"woollen hats, scarves, gloves, bed socks and some nights it was so cold that we also wore our dressing gowns"*.

In the morning they would have to break the ice on top of their washing water in a jug on an old-fashioned wash-stand. Before attending lectures at 9am, there were chores to complete after tidying their rooms and making beds; these included cleaning bathrooms, washing dishes and laying the table. They also had to make butter pats, which was a challenge to most! Even after starting work on the wards, probationers would still be based in Cross House for a while and have to trek across what was known as the "little moor" in time for breakfast in the Infirmary before commencing duty at 07.00 very often until 21.00 with only two hours off duty in the morning from 10.00 to noon. They received no pay for the first three months, during which time they had to rely on an allowance from their parents. The training lasted for four years (as it did until well into 1960s), working the final year as a staff nurse.

From 1938 all potential nursing candidates who did not have the school certificate or equivalent were required to pass a General Nursing Council (GNC) exam. This did not present any problems for the recruitment of probationers to the Infirmary. On the outbreak of war, Sister Murray[3] joined the Queen Alexandra Imperial Military Nursing Service (QAIMNS) and Sister A M Smith, since 1935 Assistant Home Sister and Assistant Tutor, became Acting Tutor with Miss M V Lupton, SRN RSCN being appointed Sister Tutor in 1944. Sister Murray decided at the end of the war to continue her career in the QAIMNS and in April 1946 Miss Muriel Dixon was appointed Sister Tutor. In 1945 Framlington House was given to the Infirmary and subsequently became the base for the Preliminary Training School.

The early years of Miss Charteris's term of office were a time of both refurbishment and extension of the hospital with several of the long-promised building developments coming to fruition. In 1931 the Runciman Wing of the Nurses' Home was opened increasing accommodation from 110 to 260 rooms and new accommodation was also opened for 28 resident medical staff.

That same year, on the site of the former Ministry of Pensions Hospital, the Leazes Hospital was opened as a pay-bed facility comprising an operating theatre and three pavilion wards providing 86 beds. Charges for these wards varied according to whether patients opted for care in a long ward, small ward or single room, that is Pavilions 1, 2, or 3 respectively. In 1933 the Orthopaedic

Building was opened, providing 48 beds in two wards (17 & 18), an operating theatre, out-patient department and fully equipped Massage School. Also in 1933 Wards 19 and 20, which had been built on top of Wards 10 and 12, were opened providing 60 beds and replacing Wards 5a & 6a, the two wooden pavilions constructed during the First World War. The designation of these additional wards is summarised in Table 28.

Ward		Name	Specialty	Comments
17	Male		Orthopaedic	
18	Female & Children		Orthopaedic	
19	Male	Rutherford Morison	Surgery	Honorary Surgeon
20	Female	Innes Hopkins Memorial Ward	Surgery	In memory of sons killed in the War
Pavilions		**Leazes Hospital**	**Pay-bed Section**	
1		The Bewick Wing, including the Hannah Ochiltree Ward and the Stirling Newall Ward		Benefactors Vice President of RVI
2		The Shipley Wing including the Watson Ward for children		Benefactors
3		The G J Fenwick Wing		Benefactors

Table 28. Designation of the additional wards opened in the RVI, 1931 & 1933

In spite of these developments, and several others not specified here, by 1935 it was recognised that there needed to be further extensions to the Infirmary to meet increased demands. Earlier in 1934 applications from both the Princess Mary Maternity Hospital (PMMH) and the Babies Hospital had been proposed and approved to build new hospitals on the site of the Infirmary. This proposal, at least in part reflected the difficulties charities faced during the years of depression in raising money for extensions and new equipment. In May 1939 a joint Hospital Appeal[4] was launched to fund the building of a Hospital Centre on the Castle Leazes site. This facility was to include the RVI, the PMMH, the Fleming Memorial Hospital for Sick Children, the Babies Hospital, the Ear Nose and Throat Hospital and the Eye Hospital. It would be many years before this initiative came to fruition although by 1945 and 1946 respectively the charities supporting the PMMH and the Babies Hospital had amalgamated with the RVI.

The 1930s also heralded an increase in the hospital's convalescent facilities. In 1933 Castle Hill in Wylam was gifted to the Infirmary by Mr Geoffrey Stirling Newall in memory of his parents, after which the decision was taken to dispose of the Innes Hopkins Home in Ryton. Ward 20 in the Infirmary was subsequently designated the Innes Hopkins Memorial Ward. Castle Hill was converted to provide accommodation initially for 35 patients but this was increased to 50 beds by 1936 and 100 by 1938 following the building of a 50 bed extension. In 1935 the Newall family also gifted Grey Court, a residence in Riding Mill to the Infirmary as a Convalescent Home for 25 children; unfortunately this home was completely destroyed by fire in 1940.

Overcrowding of the wards continued to be a problem and waiting lists were lengthening. General practitioners were notified that prior to the referral of patients to the Infirmary they must first ascertain whether a bed would be available. Likewise there was concern that many of the patients presenting at out-patients could be adequately dealt with by the general practitioners and that the casual and out-patient departments, except for emergencies, were for services of a special nature that were not available elsewhere. Road traffic accidents continued to rise and consume resources.

Following the Road Traffic Act of 1930, the Voluntary Hospitals received payments from insurance companies where there was liability in respect of

Castle Hill, Wylam, 1933

injuries to third parties requiring treatment. This scheme did not prove too successful and various amendments to the Act followed until in 1935, hospitals could claim 12/6d regardless of liability for every person brought into hospital following a motor vehicle accident. Soon however, in anticipation of war, the Infirmary had to prepare for the reception of military casualties as well as those from the local population.

Miss Charteris had relinquished her position as Principal Matron to the 1NGH in 1937, and although no record has been found regarding this, her resignation may have been associated with the setting up of an Emergency Hospital Service in 1938. The country was divided up into Sectors, each with its own Sector Matron and administrative staff based on a teaching hospital. This initiative no doubt had some impact on Miss Charteris's role during the course of the war.

On the outbreak of war in September 1939, the Infirmary like other urban hospitals responded by discharging and evacuating patients whilst they prepared for an influx of casualties. Gas attacks were expected and a decontamination unit was built along with air-raid shelters. Like other hospitals, the Infirmary benefitted financially from the Government Emergency Medical Service contributions. The Infirmary was designated a 'Casualty Clearing Station' and a number of beds were earmarked for the reception of war casualties. The bed complement at the time, including the Pay-bed section, was 710 and an initial 390 beds were supplied by the Ministry of Health for emergency use, bringing the total to 1100. Following initial preparations, the Infirmary quickly resumed normal service but with some limitations.

By 1941 Wards 2 and 5, both surgical wards, and half of Ward 8, one of the children's wards, were vacated and reserved for the reception of air-raid casualties, providing a total of 74 beds. The following December it was agreed that 32 of these would be used for traumatic injury, whether caused by enemy action or otherwise. Meanwhile, to compensate for this loss of surgical beds each of the four male medical wards was allocated six beds for the use of the surgeons. As during the First World War, many members of staff were recruited to HM Forces; it was noted in 1942 that 10 of the surgeons and physicians along with 17 registrars had enlisted. Newly qualified doctors were called up immediately but those with a junior hospital appointment were allowed six months' deferment.

Those staff remaining in the Infirmary had to cope not only with the consequent depletion in their number but also the extra burden of additional duties which they were required to undertake in supporting designated war hospitals in the locality. In order to further reduce some of the pressures accentuated by the war in 1942 the Infirmary introduced an appointments system for GP referred outpatient consultations.

The actual number of nursing staff from the Infirmary who enlisted on the outbreak of war is unknown, however the previous year 28 were recorded to be registered with either the TANS or the Naval Reserve, and by 1942 56 members of the 'lay staff' had enlisted. Certainly the profile of the nursing complement of the Infirmary underwent changes between the years 1939 and 1940, with a new grade of nursing auxiliary introduced as the nursing service was augmented by approximately 50 members of the British Red Cross Association and the Civil Nursing Reserve.

The Civil Nursing Reserve (CNR) 1939-1945

In 1937, anticipation of war, the Chief Medical Officer of Health established an Emergency Nursing Committee. Arising from this the Royal College of Nursing, the British Red Cross Society and the Order of St John were tasked with the job of compiling a register of assistant nurses and nursing auxiliaries and organising a Civil Nursing Reserve to provide additional nursing staff to care for civilian casualties in the event of war. By the outbreak of war it had recruited 7000 trained nurses, 3000 assistant nurses and 20,000 auxiliary nurses. While the assistant nurses were those with some nursing experience there was no means available to ascertain what training they may or may not have received. The nursing auxiliaries did not require previous experience but were provided with a short course of instruction, usually taking the form of two weeks' theoretical and practical training in a hospital at Government expense. Recruits could be either full or part time and allocated to work in hospitals, first aid posts, evacuation trains, wartime nurseries, or reception areas for those evacuated from dangerous areas. Those nursing auxiliaries employed full time (48 hours a week) and working in hospital were paid £55 a year along with free board, lodging and laundry, or a cash allowance in place of these. This was more than many nurses employed by the hospitals were receiving, moreover the Ministry of Health had now become the part employer of some nurses in most hospitals.

During the Second World War the Voluntary Aid Detachments (VADs) introduced during the previous war were used primarily in military hospitals at home and overseas.

The Civil Nursing Reserve, formed to respond to the needs of the Second World War, proved to be a catalyst for a number of changes impacting on the nursing workforce. Following the introduction of nursing auxiliaries on to the staff after the onset of war, by 1944 assistant nurses had also become a feature of the Infirmary's nursing service as Table 29 overleaf illustrates.

One of the repercussions arising from this led to a closer scrutiny at national level of the role of the assistant nurse. In 1942 'The Horder Report'[5] recommended that the assistant nurse be enrolled with the GNC and that

	Nursing Auxiliaries	Nursing Assistants
1939	0	0
1940	47	0
1941	55	0
1942	44	0
1943	57	0
1944	42	25
1945	20	12
1946	6	8
1947	16	8
1948/9	0	15

Table 29
Changes in the numbers of Nursing Auxiliaries and Nursing Assistants, 1939-1948

specific hospitals be identified to provide two-year courses of training. Thus in 1943 the State Enrolled Assistant Nurse[6] was given statutory recognition. In 1941 the GNC had given approval for the RVI to train male nurses and this was subsequently extended for a further two years. Until 1943 registration with the GNC was optional for qualified nurses, however after this time it became compulsory for all nurses to register and only those on the register were entitled to use the title 'nurse'.

By 1945 the Infirmary was employing two male staff nurses and nine male probationers. Following the end of the war the Ministry of Health instigated a scheme of short intensive training courses leading to examination for State Registration for recently demobilised men and women who had substantial experience of nursing in the military services. The Infirmary agreed to offer 50 places for such applicants. Table 30 shows how over the span of Miss Charteris's time in office the grade mix of the nursing staff in the Infirmary

Grades	1929	1946
Matron	1	1
Assistant Matron	1	1
Administrative Sisters	5	4
Ward & Dept. Sisters	24	38
Staff Nurses	33	23
Staff Nurses - Male	-	2
Probationers	133	301
Probationers - Male	-	9
Assistant Nurses	-	8
Auxiliary Nurses	-	6
	197	382

Table 30. Changes in Nursing Grade Mix 1929-1946

changed, with the most notable increase being in the number of probationer nurses.

Another of the repercussions arising from the formation of the Civil Nursing Reserve related to the pay and conditions of the nursing profession as a whole. During the late 1930s these had become a matter of increasing concern both locally and nationally. At this time these issues were still a matter for individual hospitals and were often driven by how successful they were in recruiting staff. The voluntary hospitals, especially those associated with medical schools, tended to find this easier than the municipal hospitals, which had developed from the old poor law infirmaries. In 1936 the hours of the Infirmary's night nurses were reduced from 66 to 54 per week, giving two nights off a month rather than one and this had required the employment of an additional five nurses. In 1938 it was agreed to reduce the working hours of the nursing staff to 48 hours as soon as sufficient nurses could be engaged. This necessitated the employment of 50 additional nurses and until further extensions to the Nurses' Home were completed accommodation needed to be found outside the Infirmary. The following year's Annual Report did show an increase of 37 nurses, most of whom were probationers. Brenda McBryde[7] who trained in the Infirmary described the situation in 1941 with staff at the Infirmary working longer hours for less pay in comparison to other hospitals in the country including the Newcastle General Hospital (NGH). Nurses in the NGH worked a 48-hour week while those in the Infirmary were allegedly still working 67 hours each week on day duty and 72 hours on night duty. Moreover the first year probationers were paid £25 per annum at the NGH while those in the Infirmary were paid £20. This of course was at a time when full-time nursing auxiliaries employed by the Civil Nursing Reserve were being paid £55 a year for a 48-hour week. Following the formation of a local branch of the Nurses' Guild, affiliated to the Trade Union Congress, improvements were negotiated and in July 1942 the Infirmary also joined the Federated Superannuation Scheme for Nurses and Hospital Officers with the employee and employer paying 5% and 10% respectively. The following April the Infirmary adopted the recommendations of the Rushcliffe Committee[8] and adjusted the annual salaries of the nursing staff, including board residence and laundry, as follows:

Matrons	£450-£700 (500 or more beds and GNC approved for nurse training)
Ward Sisters	£130-£180
Staff Nurses	£100-£140
Student Nurses	£40-£50

These salaries were based on a general acceptance of a 96-hour fortnight, the provision of at least one complete day off each week, 28 days' paid holiday leave each year, and a living-out allowance for nurses. The latter did not apply to students, Matrons and Assistant Matrons. From now on the pay and conditions of nurses working in the Infirmary were those as recommended nationally, with some of the costs being reimbursed by the Ministry of Health.

It was at this time that the responsibility for the management of the Infirmary's housekeeping, catering and laundry services were transferred after 190 years from the umbrella of nursing to specific departmental managers. Other changes which occurred towards the end of Miss Charteris's term of office in late 1945 and early 1946 were: withdrawal of the rule regarding the nurses having to wear black stockings; Sisters, for the first time, were given permission to be non-resident (since 1937 they had been allowed to use their own discretion regarding what time they returned to the Nurses' Home in the evening); and probationers were re-classified as student nurses.

Table 31 provides an insight into the expansion of the services provided by the Infirmary during Miss Charteris's tenure of office including a doubling of the numbers of nurses.

	1928	1946
Total number of nurses	197	382
Beds available	542*	606**
Average number of beds occupied	600	608.43
Maximum number of beds occupied	653	691
Average Length of Stay (days)	15.1	11.28
Admissions	14,469	18,710
Out-Patient Attendances	388,897	325,628
Operations performed (In & Out Patients)	15,836	16,158
Patients on the Waiting List	1932	2330
*Excludes 30 beds in Innes Hopkins Memorial Home, Ryton		
**Excludes Pay beds, Castle Hill Wylam & Babies Hospital		

Table 31. Changes in levels of patient activity and nurse staffing levels, 1928-1946

Miss Charteris was another Matron who steered the Infirmary's nursing service through the pressures and demands of a world war, although this latest conflict had brought the risks of air-raids and gas attacks much nearer home. Her tenure of service was also a period of major capital development within the Infirmary as it continued to respond to further advances in medical science. Alongside all of this there was an increased recognition of the variations in the pay and working conditions of nurses, and employers, even if they were charitable foundations, had to recognise that those who had a 'vocation' to nurse also needed reasonable remuneration and leisure time. As evidenced previously the Matron and nurses of the Infirmary willingly supported relevant 'good' causes and during the 1930s Miss Charteris made several donations to the Florence Nightingale Scholarships Fund, which had been established to provide annual scholarships for nurses, on behalf of the nursing staff.

In 1945 Miss Charteris indicated her intention of retiring at the end of March the following year, however she remained in post until November 1946, by which time she had served over eighteen years as Matron of the Infirmary. Following her retirement, she moved to Folkestone in Kent. She died aged 82 years in 1967 in Hastings, Sussex leaving £1200.

Brenda McBryde, who commenced her nursing training at the Infirmary in 1938, remembers the Matron as *"an omnipotent, plump little figure, all starch and cleanliness, with a starched white bow under her dimpled chin and high pitched voice that wobbled in agitation"*. Sister Carling writing in the 1967 'Nurses League Magazine', recalled that *"she had a finger firmly on the pulse of the hospital, and indeed, little passed that she did not know about. I think it is true to say that Miss Charteris had the respect of all her staff"*

Matron Charteris with the sisters prior to her retirememnt in 1946

Timeline

1930 The Boards of Guardians established in 1834 were abolished when their powers and responsibilities were passed to local and national government bodies.

1935 Sulphonamide drugs were the first antibiotics.

1937 The Newcastle News Theatre opened on Pilgrim Street, and in due course the Tyneside Coffee Rooms were incorporated into the building – a popular meeting spot for off-duty nurses!

1941 Discovery of the antibiotic streptomycin.

1942 The Beveridge Report was published and recommended a comprehensive state welfare system to slay the five giants of "want, disease, squalor, ignorance and idleness" This laid the foundation of the post-war welfare state and would be funded through National Insurance.

1942 The house governor's house near the entrance to the RVI was converted into the Children's Clinic.

1943 Edward Heath, who went on to become Prime Minister, had surgery in the RVI for appendicitis and was a patient in Ward 19.

---

[1] Mary Batey was born in Newcastle in 1884 and entered the Infirmary as a probationer nurse in 1907-1910. She served as staff nurse before becoming Assistant Matron at Stannington Sanatorium. From 1914-1920 she served in the TANS, re-entering the Infirmary as a Ward Sister in 1920. Prior to taking up the position of Assistant Matron in 1928 she had held the positions of Housekeeper Sister as well as Nurses' Home & Linen Room Sister. She retired in August 1945 and died in the Infirmary in 1948; the Annual Report of that year noted that she "gave incomparable devotion to her profession and to the service of the Infirmary. Her memory will long be treasured with the very greatest affection."
[2] M Johnston (nee Furniss) & E Anderson (nee Dawson)
[3] Eva Doris Murray In 1944 she was awarded the Associated Royal Red Cross (ARRC) for services in Italy. The citation read that "on the nights of February 14, 18, and 22 1944, on Anzio bridgehead, when bombs were bursting all around the camp, Sister Murray completed tours of all wards, supervising her patients and staff, with a complete disregard for her own personal safety. Her magnificent devotion to duty did much in reassuring the patients. Her administration and tactful supervision of the nursing officers and orderlies was excellent and was in keeping with the best Florence Nightingale tradition".
[4] Hospital Appeal: The daughter-in-law of Mrs Ethel Bedford Fenwick, Mary Beatrice, was on the Fleming Children's Hospital's negotiating Committee.
[5] Horder Report: Nursing Reconstruction Committee 1942
[6] State Enrolled Nurse: In 1961 'Assistant' was removed from the title. The RVI did not start to train SENs until 1968
[7] McBryde, Brenda, 'A Nurse's War', Hogarth Press, 1986. Brenda trained in the RVI 1938-1943
[8] Rushcliffe Committee, the Report of the Nurses' Salaries Committee 1943

MISS GERTRUDE LANG DAVIS
Matron and Superintendent of Nurses 1946-1948

Gertrude Lang Davis was born in Kensington on 10 April 1898 - the third of Walter and Mary Davis's four children. Her father was an assistant manager in a music hall before having his own business in Newport as an animated picture entertainer. Her mother's maiden name was Lang.

Gertrude undertook nurse training at St. Bartholomew's Hospital, London 1923-1927 and midwifery training at Queen Charlotte's Hospital, London qualifying in 1928. She had served five years as a Nursing Sister at the Civil General Hospital Rangoon, Burma and three years as Matron-Superintendent at the International Hospital Kobe, Japan.

Whilst nursing overseas Gertrude visited hospitals in Canada, New Zealand, Australia, Malay Straits, Ceylon, China, India, and South Africa. She held the certificate in Housekeeping and Administration awarded by the Leicester Royal Infirmary where she had also provided holiday cover for the second Assistant Matron. In 1940 Gertrude was working as Matron-Superintendent at the Northallerton Emergency Hospital and in October 1941 her appointment to the post of Matron-Superintendent at the Royal Victoria Hospital, Dover was announced. She had also been a Technical Nursing Officer to the Ministry of Labour.

It seems that Gertrude may have inherited some of her father's interest in the theatre; whilst Matron in Northallerton she was the producer of the two performances of the pantomime 'Aladdin' given on Christmas Day, 1940.

In January 1946 there were reports in the local press that the Infirmary had received over 200 inquiries in response to the advertisement for the post of Matron. However it was not until May, and following interviews of many of the candidates, that Gertrude's appointment to the post was announced. She took up the role just a few days before the announcement on 6 November 1946 that the proposals for the introduction of a National Health Service had been passed by HM Government to provide a comprehensive health service with free treatment for all at the point of delivery.

Gertrude's time in post coincided with the 40th Anniversary of the opening of the RVI as well as the last full year of the Infirmary as a voluntary institution prior to it being handed over to the National Health Service. It is therefore fitting to illustrate, as shown in Table 32, the growth that had taken place during the 40 years following the transfer of services from the Forth Banks to the Royal Victoria Infirmary. Worthy of particular note is the generous support that the Infirmary received from the working men of the area.

	1907	1947
Beds	420	600
In-patients	6,445	19,333
Out-patients	93,244	336,452
Operations	5,678	18,026
Average length of stay (days)	19	11.42
Nurses	124	377
Resident Medical Staff	10	26
Expenditure	£30,000	£386,920
Workmen's Subscriptions	£10,877	£126,788

Table 32 Comparison of the Infirmary's growth indicators 1907-1947

Although Gertrude's time at the Infirmary was short, some significant developments of relevance to nursing took place during her term of office. In 1947 the House Committee agreed to accept colonial applicants for nurse training providing that the numbers did not exceed 4-6 at any one time, and Framlington House was furnished and equipped as the Preliminary Training School providing accommodation for a Sister Tutor and 20 student nurses. Other properties in Framlington Place were purchased about this same time to relieve pressure on the Nurses' Home. Also in 1948 two houses in Leazes Terrace, numbers 34 & 35, became the new base for the Babies Hospital[1], which had amalgamated with the Infirmary in 1944. The houses were adapted to provide accommodation for 12 babies and 8 mothers.

Gertrude was guest of honour on the occasion of the Annual Prize-Giving at Tynemouth Infirmary in July of that year and in her speech she said: "*We are on the verge of a revolutionary change in the nursing profession…the change will need a great deal of reorganisation. We are going a step forward as a body of professional women – women who are going to bring the nursing profession to the front rank as a career for women. We have a future that we have to make. We are the pioneers of this National Health Service of ours*".

Gertrude faced opposition to several of her proposals for change and there were concerns about her general demeanour. On the basis that there was a supply of uniform dress material for at least another two years, she failed to

A view of the Royal Victoria Infirmary showing the Nurses' Home and, in the far top left corner, Framlington House can just be seen

Sister Tutor Miss Dixon with student nurses wearing Miss Lang Davis's red buttons. Courtesy of Diane Alderdice, whose mother features in the photograph

gain approval for changing the nurses' uniforms to white dresses with American caps replacing the butterfly caps worn by the student nurses. Her ideas in respect of introducing a three-shift system for the nurses also failed to gain support. She had introduced, without approval, a new intermediate grade of 'charge nurse' and questions were asked about the red buttons which she expected all newly appointed students to wear so that she would always be able to distinguish them as 'her nurses'! In September 1947 she was asked to submit a written report for the Nursing Committee, however this did not satisfy the Committee and a fuller report was requested resulting in Gertrude tendering her resignation with three months' notice in December 1947 due to *"increasing responsibilities at home to which she must devote herself"*

The Infirmary's Annual Report for 1947 recorded Gertrude's resignation and the House Committee recorded their appreciation for her services during her period of office. In 1948 Gertrude was one of the 14 Regional Nurses appointed. Initially she held the position for the Sheffield Regional Hospital Board, but by 1951 she had taken up the equivalent post with the East Anglian Board. In October 1969, and following a long illness, Gertude aged 71 years, died in Cambridge leaving £7589. Her death was noted in the RVI Nurses' League Magazine the following year.

---

[1] The Babies Hospital had during the war re-located from West Parade in Newcastle to Blagdon Hall in Northumberland.

MISS JANET THOMSON HUTTON
Assistant Matron, 1945-1948
Matron 1948-1959

Janet Thomson Hutton was born in Abdie, Fifeshire, Scotland in June 1897; she was the fifth of seven children born to George and Christina Hutton. Her father was a native of Fifeshire and described in 1901 as a 'farm grieve'; as such he would have taken his orders from the farmer, but would be in charge of the rest of the farm workers. Her mother originated from Caithness.

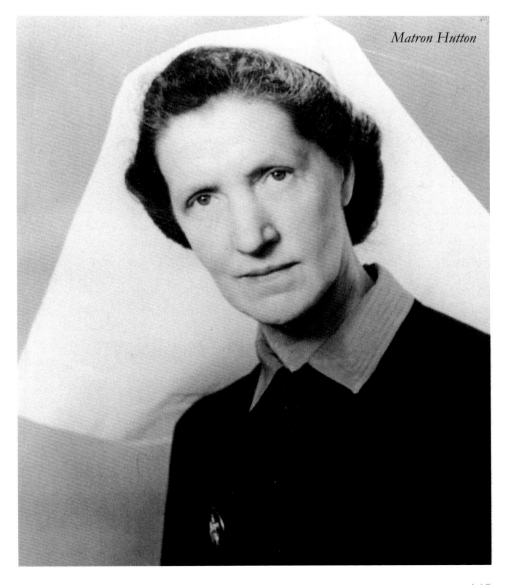

Matron Hutton

In 1901 the family were living in Abdie but by the time Janet commenced school they lived at Newington. Janet attended Rathillet School from October 1904 and in August 1906 she was enrolled in the Moonzie Public School. In November 1910 she transferred to a school in Dunfermline. From June 1917 until February 1919 Janet was employed in the Rosyth Dockyard. Subsequently she spent two years at the Church of Scotland Women's College. By the 1930s two of her brothers, George and Sinclair, were fruiterers in Newcastle with businesses in the Grainger Market and Clayton Street.

Janet undertook her nurse training at the Infirmary from 1924 to 1928, registering with the General Nursing Council in April 1928. Following qualification, she held positions in the Infirmary as Sister on Ward 7, Night Sister, and in 1935 was appointed Housekeeping Sister.

She served in the Middle East with the Territorial Army Nursing Service during the Second World War and returned to the Infirmary in October 1945 when she was appointed to the post of Assistant Matron, a post which was subsequently designated Deputy Matron. In May 1948 she was appointed Matron, and on 5 July 1948, after 197 years as a Voluntary Hospital, the control, premises and equipment of the Infirmary were transferred to the Minister of Health under the National Health Service Act of 1946.

The Royal Victoria Infirmary, now formally designated a Teaching Hospital, and along with the Princess Mary Maternity Hospital, the Newcastle upon Tyne Dental Hospital and the Babies Hospital, became the United Newcastle upon Tyne Hospitals. Under these new arrangements the House Committee was replaced by a Board of Governors. Membership of the Board comprised representatives from the University of Durham, the Newcastle Regional Hospital Board, and the medical and dental staff. Some Board members were appointed but others were nominated by their constituency.

However the transition from charity to state ownership was smoothed with twenty-three of the twenty-nine members of the Board having given previous service on one or other of the member hospitals' previous committees; also the Chairman, appointed by the Minister of Health, had previously served as Vice-Chairman to the Infirmary's House Committee. There were three women on the Board including Viscountess Ridley, with the House Governor taking minutes and Matron usually "in attendance".

Two of the first essentials of the NHS were in respect of the provision of national salary scales and conditions of service for all employees and formalising its relationship in respect of the nursing services. The Whitley Council and the Nurses Act 1949 were the means by which these were achieved.

Whitley Council

The Whitley Council system, which had been used in the Civil Service since 1920, was adopted in 1949 to negotiate pay and conditions of work within the hospital service. The Whitley Councils of the Health Service consisted of a General Council and nine functional councils, one of which was the Nurses and Midwives Council. Each of the nine functional councils comprised members from both management and staff organisations appointed by the Minister of Health. The outcome of the first round of negotiations was to change the basis on which nurses were paid. Traditionally hospital nurses received a net salary and were provided with free board and lodging. The Whitley agreement introduced gross salaries, and nurses were then required to pay for their board and lodgings at rates laid down nationally.

The Nurses Act 1949

This set the foundation for a number of changes including: from 1951 the closing of the Register of Male Nurses and integrating registered male nurses into the General Part of the Register; giving probationer nurses recognition as student nurses and emphasising the need to focus more on their educational needs, which had previously tended to be subordinated to the service needs of the hospitals; and the establishment in 1951 of Area Nurse Training Committees in each of the 14 Regional Hospital Boards areas for England and Wales. Their purpose was to advise and assist the training institutions in their area on all matters connected to the training of nurses; to advise and assist the General Nursing Council in matters relating to the approval of training institutions; and to promote improvements and research into training methods, which included the power to initiate experimental schemes of training.

Miss Hutton and Miss H I Powell Thompson, who at that time was a Nurse Tutor in the Infirmary, were both among the 15 members appointed to the Area Nurse Training Committee for the Newcastle Regional Hospital Board. Nurse training was now open to much more scrutiny than in the past and it became increasingly important for the training schools to be seen to be offering attractive courses.

During 1948 Miss M Jackson had been appointed Senior Tutor, introducing the block system of training in 1950 and abolishing the requirement for nurses to attend lectures in their own time. The Teaching Unit, an annex close to the Nurses' Home, was provided in the early 1950s and groups of about 30 student nurses would spend short periods of lectures and practical instruction for up to a month at a time in between periods of practical experience on the wards and departments. From 1948 the annual intake of students nurses was increased from 80 to 120.

Following the Second World War and the increasing awareness of the need to relieve student nurses of tasks now regarded as 'non-nursing' the grade mix of the Infirmary's nursing team continued to evolve to include both more men and more part-time staff as shown in Table 33. The Infirmary witnessed

	1947	1952
Charge Nurses		4
Male Staff Nurses	2	11
Male Student Nurses	21	15
Male Assistant Nurses		6
Male Ward Orderlies		36
Part Time Staff Nurses	4	17
Part Time Assistant Nurses		6
Total number of Student Nurses	**280**	**348**
Total number of Nursing Staff	**337**	**625**

Table 33. The changing face of the Infirmary's nursing workforce 1947 - 1952

a steady increase in the numbers of men recruited into its nursing workforce being most noticeable within the ranks of the student nurses and the ward orderlies. This period also marked the beginning of the opportunities for part-time nursing staff and by 1956 out of 721 nursing staff 280 were non-resident. In April 1959 nursing hours were reduced to 44 hours per week; however the transition was not without difficulties with the senior staff working longer hours than previously to enable the junior nurses to go off duty as scheduled.

Three notable charge-nurses who trained in the Infirmary during Miss Hutton's term of office were: Harry Pinkney on Ward 19, Fred Smith on Theatres and John Ritson on Ward 4; who qualified in 1948, 1949 and 1955 respectively. Two other notable and much respected personalities who joined the ranks of the Infirmary's staff at this time were: Miss E Clapham, formerly a catering officer with the National Coal Board, who from 1950 to 1968 was the Infirmary's much loved catering officer; and 'Sister' M Freeman, a dietician, who had trained at the Queen Elizabeth Hospital in Birmingham and came to the Infirmary to take charge of the Diet Kitchen. Over the course of her 22 years at the Infirmary Sister Freeman coaxed many student nurses through their invalid cookery course.

Some senior members of the Nurses' League have recalled memories of their days as student nurses during the early days of Matron Hutton's reign. Those who had entered the Preliminary Training School (PTS) prior to November 1947 had been supplied with sufficient material for six uniform dresses and 24 aprons all of which had to be made up according to the RVI regulation pattern. Now they were provided with their uniform dress and aprons which, for hygienic purposes, could never be worn outside the hospital; the caps were known as 'butterflies or duck bottoms' and a challenge to fold and make up. Brown stockings and brown rubber-soled shoes completed the uniform.

Six weeks were spent in PTS under instruction from two Sister Tutors. There were lectures on anatomy and physiology, health and hygiene and visits to sewage works. Practical instruction was given on everything from all the variations of bed-making and bandaging, blanket bathing, the prevention of pressure sores, the art of giving a bedpan, and practising the method of giving injections with an orange.

Once on the wards and after the morning rush of breakfasts, bed-making and blanket bathing it was off "to dress" – that is coffee time and changing into a clean apron. The junior student spent much time cleaning in the sluice including the sorting, counting and bagging of linen – all soiled linen having been sluiced and scrubbed beforehand. Later the student would progress to setting trolleys for various procedures and attending to the patients' dressings, meanwhile the tasks continued, but now it was the cleaning, checking and sterilising of glass syringes and needles along with other surgical equipment. Rolls of gauze had to be cut into squares for dressings and cotton wool made into balls for swabbing.

The third year students gained considerable experience by having to take charge of the ward in the absence of the ward sister and her one staff nurse, however some experience in taking charge would also have been gained on night duty, with each ward being allocated a junior and senior student under the overall supervision of a night sister who would be covering a number of wards. One of the stresses on night-duty was trying to memorise all the patients' names, diagnoses and details of their progress prior to the night sister's first round at about 11pm. Apart from long hours in the wards, students also had to attend lectures in their free time. They quickly adapted to the unwritten rules of the hospital etiquette: learning never to walk through a door in front of someone more senior; never using Christian names; always following Sister in order of seniority to the dining room where, before taking a seat, everyone waited for an acknowledgement from Matron, hopefully before she had said grace.

Matron was the key figure in the hospital and did a daily round on each ward; probationers went weak at the knees when seeing her approach, hopefully "*the stockings were ladder free, the shoes polished and the cap straight*".

Students were accommodated in the Nurses' Home and under the watchful eye of the Home Sister who by means of a system of 'passes' controlled when, how often, and for how late they could stay out. By 1950 all the nursing sisters were housed in off-site accommodation leaving the "collegiate" atmosphere of the Nurses' Home for more homely dwellings shared with a small group of colleagues.

Monday	No visiting	18.30 – 19.00
Tuesday	No visiting	18.30 – 19.00
Wednesday	14.00 - 1600	14.00 – 15.00
Thursday	No visiting	18.30 – 19.00
Friday	No visiting	No visiting
Saturday	14.00 - 1600	14.00 – 15.00
Sunday	14.00 - 1600	14.00 – 16.00

Table 34. Visiting hours in the late 1940s

Visiting hours, which are set out in Table 34, were strictly enforced at this time although coinciding with the transfer of services to the NHS the frequency changed from three days a week to six days a week. The visitors' entrance, which gave access onto the corridor of the Infirmary close to Ward 1, was still in use; however before the ward doors were opened, the wards had to be tidied, the patients made comfortable and everything put in order.

Some of the innovations introduced in the 1950's included a patient's trolley shop operated by the British Red Cross Society; an electric tractor to haul the meal trolleys from the kitchen to the wards; and in 1958, following a GNC inspection, it was ruled that the sluicing, sorting and counting of linen should be carried out away from the wards and not undertaken by student nurses, a Central Linen Bank was opened with the large percentage of linen being 'pooled' rather than allocated to specific wards and departments. The latter would have been a boon for junior students.

There was a programme of activities arranged for the week of the Bicentenary Celebration in May 1951, which included a reunion meeting for former nursing staff with lectures, department visits, lunch and a tea party. Later that evening there was a concert in the canteen directed by the Nurses and Housemen. On Wednesday 23 May 1951, and two hundred years after a house in

Matron Hutton with sisters outside St Nicholas Cathedral on the occasion of the 200th anniversary of the founding of the Infirmary and, below, cutting the cake at the reception

Gallowgate had been opened for the reception of patients, Miss Hutton the twentieth Matron of the Infirmary, accompanied by her Assistants and many of the Ward Sisters attended the Service of Thanksgiving in the Cathedral Church of St Nicholas. Miss Hutton and a number of Sisters were guests at a celebratory luncheon held in the Old Assembly Rooms. On the Saturday a Garden Party for staff was held in the Exhibition Park.

Throughout her time in post Miss Hutton had been assisted in her role by Dorothy Horsborough[1] and Olive Irene Allsopp[2], but also from 1952 by Dorothy M Pratt[3]. Miss Hutton retired in 1959 and was invited to join the Annual dinner of the Infirmary's Medical Staff Committee. In her letter of thanks to the Committee she wrote in January 1960: *"I wish to thank you for a most enjoyable evening and for giving me another opportunity to meet again many members of the Consultant Staff of the Royal Victoria Infirmary. I enjoyed my work at the hospital and my position as Matron was made much easier by the friendliness of the medical staff towards me, by their unfailing interest in nursing problems, by their loyal support during my term of office. I would be most grateful if you would let all members of the Medical Staff concerned, know how much I appreciated their kindness in inviting me as their guest to the Annual Dinner and also thank them for the lovely gift they presented to me on that occasion. In my retirement I now look back with very happy memories of the RVI"*

Miss Hutton was nominated by Miss Shaw to be the founder chairman of the RVI Nurses' League, however this was turned down in favour of Miss Shaw taking on the role. She died aged 79 years in 1977, at which time she was living in Ponteland; she left £12795.

Timeline

1948   The Dental Hospital and School transferred from the RVI into the former home of the Medical School on Northumberland Road.

1953   Coronation of HM Queen Elizabeth II.

1953   James Watson and Francis Crick at Cambridge University describe the structure of the DNA.

---

[1] Dorothy Horsborough Deputy Matron, was born in 1890. She trained in the Infirmary 1920-1923 and in 1939 she was a Sister in the RVI. She became an Assistant Matron in 1948 and subsequently became Deputy Matron. She retired in 1954. She was a founder member of the RVI Nurses' League serving on the committee as deputy chairman for ten years from 1959 to 1969 subsequently becoming Vice-President. She died May 1981.

[2] Olive Irene Allsopp was born in 1906, she obtained her RFN qualification in 1929 at Seacroft City Hospital in Leeds prior to training in the RVI 1930-1933. In 1939 she was a Sister in the RVI and was appointed Assistant Matron in 1948 becoming Deputy Matron in 1954. She retired during the 1960's and died in 1976

[3] Dorothy Pratt was born in 1916 and trained in the RVI 1935 -1939. She was appointed Assistant Matron in 1952 and following 'Salmon' became a Senior Nursing Officer. She retired in 1976. She served on the RVI Nurses' League Committee from 1967 – 1994, and was Editor of the League Magazine from 1968 to 1976. She died in 2014.

MISS FREDA SHAW
Matron 1959 - 1969
Chief Nursing Officer 1969 - 1972

Freda Shaw, the daughter of George and Sarah, was born on 24 April 1912 in Saddleworth, Yorkshire. She trained at the Royal Infirmary Oldham 1931-1934 and was admitted to the Register on 23 November 1934. In 1936 Freda moved to London, undertaking midwifery training at Queen Charlotte's Hospital, before transferring to the Maida Vale Hospital for Nervous Diseases, and subsequently the West End Hospital for Nervous Diseases, Regent Park, where as a staff nurse and sister she worked on both the wards and in the operating theatre.

During 1940 Freda was a Pupil Housekeeper at the Westminster Hospital from where she moved to Addenbrooke's Hospital, Cambridge. She remained in Cambridge until 1943, working as both a relief ward sister and relief administrative sister. In 1944 she was awarded a bursary to study mental health and following this she spent about four years on active service with the Queen Alexandra Imperial Military Nursing Service Reserve (QAIMNSR).

The father of a member[1] of the RVI Nurses' League remembered meeting her in Belgium following the D-day landings in 1944 and, according to a press report in April 1959, she had also served in India. Following her return to civilian life, Freda continued as a reservist with the QAIMNS and her promotion to Lieutenant was announced in The Gazette on 10 August 1951. Between 1948 and 1949 Freda gained the Royal College of Nursing (RCN) Certificate in Hospital Administration, after which she was appointed Deputy Matron at the City General Hospital, Sheffield; a position she held until 1952 when she became Matron at the Sunderland Royal Infirmary.

Matron Shaw

In July 1959 Freda was appointed to the post of Matron at the Royal Victoria Infirmary, becoming the second, but unrelated, Matron F Shaw in Newcastle as Miss Fanny Shaw had been appointed to the Matron's post at Newcastle General Hospital in 1953. Freda reported that her two hobbies were motoring and foreign travel, which she often combined. Former nurses will recall her driving in her open top car between the RVI and Castle Hill, Wylam!

One of the first things that Miss Shaw did following her appointment to the Infirmary was to establish the RVI Nurses' League. The first meeting was held on 15 September 1959 and was attended by over 100 nurses. Miss Shaw continued as Chairman until her retirement in 1972. In 1960 Miss Shaw re-introduced the Annual Prize-Giving ceremonies which had fallen into abeyance during the war, and, for those who wished to buy one, she introduced the RVI Nurses' Scarf based on a design similar to those worn by the medical students of King's College.

The RVI League of Friends was established in March 1961 with the encouragement of Miss Shaw and the support of the Board of Governors. The League soon had over 600 members, some of whom worked as volunteers whilst others engaged in fund-raising and went on to provide a number of highly valued amenities for patients and their families. In 1965 the Hospital Shop opened and the following year the League funded the refurbishment of two rooms to provide over-night accommodation for the relatives of seriously ill patients as well as refurbishing the Mortuary Chapel.

Some insight into Matron's typical day was provided by a local reporter[2] when she shadowed Miss Shaw for a day in October 1960. At 8 am Matron received reports from the Night Sisters then, with the help of the Deputy Matron, she tackled the large amount of mail that included applications for jobs, requests for references of current or former members of staff applying for other posts, and correspondence dealing with the domestic affairs of the hospital - at this time the Matron was still responsible for some of the ancillary members of staff. As it was a Wednesday it was interviewing day for prospective student nurses and the reporter observed as Matron and the Principal Tutor, Miss Jackson[3], carefully questioned and advised the candidates. Miss Shaw observed that in her day candidates would always have worn a hat at interview!

Although not mentioned by the reporter, the candidates would also have been accompanied by their mothers, a tradition which continued well into the 1970s. After lunch Matron held a meeting with the Sisters to discuss current issues and identified those which would need to be taken to the Board of Governors. This was followed by a meeting with the House Governor & Secretary to the Board of Governors where the main topics related to planned extensions and refurbishments. There were visits to the Children's Clinic, where she was also told about the mother and baby facilities in the Babies Hospital.

Next stop was the Preliminary Training School for 36 student nurses in Framlington House, where she was introduced to the tutor in charge, Miss Dixon[4] and met up with 'Mrs Bedford and Belinda' the life-like dolls on which students practiced their skills. Finally the reporter accompanied Matron as she did her 'rounds' on the private, orthopaedic and children's wards. Although not reported, Matron, readily distinguished by her green dress, would have

Nurses prize giving 1968 with Freda Shaw (cenre front)

asked each patient "*and how are you today?*" and the accompanying nurse would have been expected to give the name and diagnosis of each patient as well as a progress report. At the end of the day Miss Shaw commented that "*nursing is my life. I love every minute of it*".

By 1964 a major refurbishment of the wards had commenced with the provision of extra toilets, bathrooms, and sitting rooms for patients and about this time part of the Nurses' Home was being converted for use as the Doctors' Residence. It was completely cut off from the Nurses' Home, having a separate access directly off the conservatory. The doors of the Nurses' Home were still being locked at 11pm with late-comers having to call the Night Sister if they were locked out.

This ruling was justified on the grounds of late nights having a detrimental effect on health – and therefore fitness for duty – but also concerns about the 'moral welfare' of the nurses. Some without late night passes would therefore, not infrequently, resort to climbing through windows conveniently left open! One hundred years on, Florence Nightingale's values were still intrinsic to many aspects of the nursing service!

Miss Shaw was notable for introducing or helping facilitate several changes which eased the work of the nursing staff. One of her early innovations was the introduction of cadet nurses. These were recruited from amongst those waiting to commence nurse training at the age of eighteen and on day-release they would attend a pre-nursing course at a local college. Some cadets were employed at the convalescent home, Castle Hill, Wylam, others helped on the children's wards and in Children's Clinic, whilst others were allocated to various departments including the Linen Room, Diet Kitchen, Messenger Service,

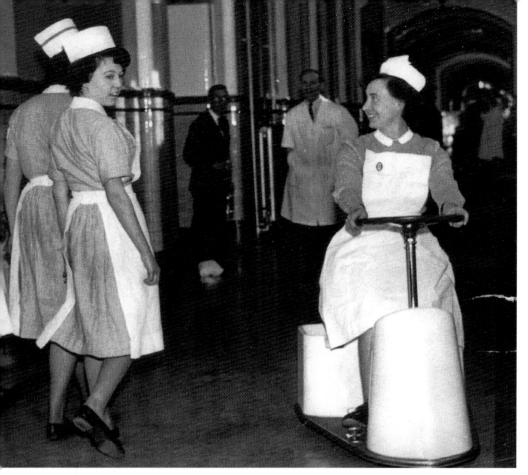

Sister Nancy Wilson on the Night Superintendant's scooter

Matron's Office, and the Central Sterile Supplies Department (CSSD).

The CSSD had been established early in 1962 with Sister K Harrison at the helm and provided the wards and departments with dressing and procedure packs as well as glass syringes and other non-disposable items. Although most needles and some syringes were by this time disposable, relief from the burden of sterilising equipment and making dressings at individual ward level was a major change in the work of the nurse.

In 1963 Miss Shaw made a three-month tour of hospitals and nurse training schools in the USA under the auspices of the World Health Organisation. The tour provided opportunities to gain some insights into the:
• Training, and organisation of nursing services, including nursing records
• Integration of married women into the nursing team
• Use of intensive, progressive and minimal care units
• Centralisation of hospital services such as catering, linen, pharmacy, central sterile supplies and the use of disposables.
Miss Shaw provided a report on her tour and whilst this did not include any

recommendations it is evident that her experience influenced some of the developments in the Infirmary over her tenure.

During the early 1960s the Night Superintendent had been supplied with a 'scooter' that speeded up her response time to emergency calls, and subsequently the night sisters were also issued with 'bleeps', enabling a much swifter response to calls for help from the student nurses in charge of the wards. In 1966 the method of serving patients' meals changed, no longer were they served individually by Sister from a trolley delivered to the ward, each patient's meal was now plated according to their individual menu[5] choice in the central kitchen and delivered to the wards on trays.

Miss Shaw also steered through a number of changes relating to the administration of medicines: a safer method of prescribing, checking and recording of medicines and drugs was introduced; in 1968 each ward was provided with a locked medicine trolley which held the current medications of each patient and could be taken directly to the bedside. Regulations regarding the administration of intravenous drugs by nurses were also established; a reflection of the increasing use of antibiotics and a reduction in the frequency of the intramuscular route of administration. It was also about this time that each ward was provided with its own resuscitation trolley.

It was during the 1960s that major advances in science and technology facilitated much greater specialisation within the practice of medicine and surgery and this inevitably impacted on the work of the Infirmary. Two of the surgical wards, Wards 5 and 6 had converted to plastic surgery and neurology wards respectively; in 1961 dermatology, which for many years had shared Ward 11 with gynaecology before moving to temporary accommodation in the basement, was relocated to Ward 21 built under Ward 1; and Pavilion 2 gradually gave up its private beds and became home to ophthalmology. Meanwhile coronary care facilities were developing on Ward 14 with, by the end of 1967, a hospital-based emergency response team using a specially equipped ambulance to attend to and stabilise patients prior to transfer to the Infirmary.

That same year the home dialysis service and a renal transplantation programme were both inaugurated and this was followed by the provision of a purpose-built regular dialysis unit and in the early 1970's with a designated Renal Transplant Theatre. It was not until August 1970 that the Infirmary opened its Intensive Therapy Unit (ITU) although some months prior to this an influenza epidemic had tested out systems when, with 120 nursing staff on sick leave and the medical wards overflowing, Ward 2 was closed and prepared to take the influenza patients; by the evening the ward was full and included eight patients on ventilators.

By 1971 the Infirmary had also added a Programmed Investigation Unit and a Child Development Centre to its portfolio of services. However that same year neonatal surgery was transferred from the Babies Hospital to the Fleming Memorial Hospital for Sick Children.

In spite of these developments the need for a new hospital was still on the agenda. It will be recalled that prior to the war a joint Hospital Appeal was launched to fund the building of a Hospital Centre on the Castle Leazes site, and over thirty years later, in April 1970, a Project Management Team was established to plan the building of a new 1,300-bed RVI. The first phase was to include a ward block of 422 beds, an out-patient department and eight operating theatres. It would be another 22 years before this phase, with many refinements on the way, came to fruition[6].

The Infirmary's School of Nursing, meanwhile, was adjusting not only to the demands placed on it from the General Nursing Council (GNC) but also the specific needs of the Infirmary. The GNC syllabus was under constant review; study blocks were increased from of 24 to 28 weeks, and secondments for obstetric, psychiatric, geriatric and community experience started to be introduced. Also, for students entering from 1970, the state final classroom-based practical exam was replaced by four ward based practical assessments.

These assessments were undertaken by the ward sisters, who in preparation for this added responsibility were required to undertake an 'Art of Examining Course'. Since 1967, in conjunction with the Newcastle Polytechnic, the Infirmary had also been providing placements for student nurses undertaking the Diploma in Hospital and Community Nursing, which in addition to State Registration would provide a district nursing and HV qualification.

The following year the Infirmary's School of Nursing had been approved by the GNC to provide training leading to enrolment, after which time the numbers of State Enrolled Nurses became an increasing and much valued feature of the Infirmary's nurse staffing complement. By 1969 the Infirmary had at total of 450 student and pupil nurses but it was also offering post-registration courses for nurses; firstly in anaesthetics, and subsequently in theatre nursing, ophthalmic nursing, and an intensive nursing skills course. All of this development served to increase the demands placed on the ward sisters. To support these new opportunities for continued professional development, Miss Shaw obtained the services of a part-time librarian from the City Library and in 1968 a well-stocked Nurses' Library was opened in the nursing administration block above Peacock Hall.

Nurses' pay and working hours were both major issues during the 1960s. During the decade working hours were reduced first to 42 hours and then from January 1970 to 40 hours a week, for the first time giving nurses two full days off each week. However, the provision of adequate nursing cover for the wards became an increasing problem which led to the employment of more part-time staff and, in particular, more nursing auxiliaries, for whom a short in-service training was introduced. Prior to this in 1962 the Royal College of Nursing was joined by the trade unions in a major public protest about nurses' pay, and nurses from the Infirmary with Miss Shaw's blessing, joined a demonstration outside parliament. Debates in parliament followed, leading to a special pay award. Table 35 summarises the improvement in nurses' salaries during Miss Shaw's time in office:

Grade	1959	1970
1st year Student Nurse	285	525
3rd year Student Nurse	320	624
Enrolled Nurse	425-545	801-969
Staff Nurse	496-621	930-1182
Ward Sister	620-800	1200-1554
Assistant Matron	1145-1360	1572-1902 (Grade 7)
Matron (1000 beds)	1910-2235	2080-2435 (Grade10a)

Table 35. Improvements in Nursing Salaries 1959-1970 (£ per annum)

In 1966 the Salmon Report of the Committee on Senior Nursing Staff Structure was published and this heralded a major restructuring of nursing management. Pilot schemes based on the recommendations were scheduled for 1967 and 1968, however the Government announced in the autumn of 1968 that the new grading structure must be in place in all hospital groups by 1969. Miss Shaw was subsequently appointed as the Chief Nursing Officer (Grade 10) of the United Newcastle upon Tyne Hospitals Group in August 1969, with responsibility for overseeing the implementation of the Salmon Structure. Senior nurses were now seconded to management courses and by the end of 1970 the restructuring of the Infirmary's nursing staff had been completed in line with the Salmon recommendations.
• Two Principal Nursing Officer (PNO Grade 9) posts were established with Miss Ovington leading the General Division and Miss M F Dixon appointed to the Education Division.
• Five Senior Nursing Officers (SNOs Grade 8) were appointed to work under Miss Ovington, three to manage designated wards and departments and another two with responsibilities for the Night Service and Allocations. Miss Dixon had a team of three SNOs (Teaching)
• Eight Nursing Officer (NOs Grade 7) posts were established with responsibility for designated wards and departments

The Report of the Committee on Senior Nursing Staff Structure (Salmon) 1966

This Committee had been set up in 1963 and its terms of reference were to advise on the senior nursing staff (ward sister and above) structure in the hospital service, the administrative functions of the respective grades, and the methods of preparing staff to occupy them. The Committee found that there was confusion about both nursing titles, which did not relate to responsibilities as well as the functions of deputies and assistants; and also that lines of communication were blurred. Demographic changes had also impacted on the profile of the ward sister, no longer typically a spinster with many years of service; by this time 47% of them were married, 17% worked part-time, and the average time spent in that role had reduced to 10 years. Three distinct levels of management were identified and a distinction made between the 'General Nursing and the Education Divisions' as follows:

First Line Management (executive)
Staff Nurse	Grade 5
Ward Sister/Charge Nurse	Grade 6

Middle Management (programmers)
Nursing Officer – Matron (NO)	Grade 7
Senior Nursing Officer (SNO)	Grade 8

Top Management (policy making)
Principal Nursing Officer (PNO)	Grade 9
Chief Nursing Officer (CNO)	Grade 10

The organisational plan was based on one nursing officer covering a span of 4-5 units of work.

The Nursing Officer post would combine advice on nursing practice with a certain amount of administration. Recommendations were given regarding the types of management courses suitable for First and Middle Line Managers. The Committee were surprised that the nursing profession occupied a secondary position within the health service and that the right of nurses to speak on nursing policy was ignored when the NHS was established. It was recommended that the top nursing managers should have seats at Board level and parity of esteem with other members of the governing body.

Meanwhile another important and exceptional local reorganisation took place when, in October 1971, the management of all the hospitals in Newcastle were united under one management to form the Newcastle University

Hospitals Group. The Infirmary, established 200 years previously, had now been subsumed into a larger organisation comprising three sectors. The Infirmary and its associated hospitals of the Babies Hospital, Castle Hill, Princess Mary Maternity Hospital, and Dental Hospital were now joined by the Sanderson Hospital and Rye Hill Hospital to form the Central Sector. This was an interim arrangement prior to further reorganisation arising out of the 1973 NHS Reorganisation Act. Miss Shaw was appointed the Chief Nursing Officer to the Group and now had much extended management responsibilities, with her former deputy taking over prime responsibility for the Infirmary.

Miss Shaw retired in July 1972 and moved to Sussex after 13 years in office. The RVI Nurses' League reported in 1973 that she had given unstintingly of herself as an administrator, organiser and advisor. She was always intensely aware of the increasing pressures and tensions experienced by the nursing staff, and worked and planned unceasingly to safeguard them as much as possible. In May 1999 she died aged 87 years, in Worthing Sussex, bequeathing £1,000 to the RVI Nurses' League.

The Conservatory in the RVI. Photo courtsey of Dorothy Tacchi

Timeline

1961   The contraceptive pill became available to married women through the NHS. It was not until 1967 that it became more widely prescribed.

1963   King's College, University of Durham, which traced its roots back to the founding in 1834 of the School of Medicine and Surgery, gained its independence to become the University of Newcastle upon Tyne, now Newcastle University.

1966   The GNC Register for Fever Nurses was closed

1967   Dr Christiaan Barnard performs the first human heart transplant

1967   The Abortion Act came into effect

1971   Decimal currency introduced on 15 February

---

[1] Diane Toop (nee Groves)

[2] Iris Keenan, a reporter for the Evening Chronicle.

[3] May Jackson OBE was educated at Dame Allan's School and undertook her nurse training in the Stamford & Rutland General Hospital. She served in the TANS during the 2nd world war and undertook a nurse tutor's course at Leeds University. She was appointed Principal Tutor to the RVI in 1948 retiring in 1969 and died aged 88 years in 1997.

[4]   Muriel Dixon trained at Leeds General Hospital and came to the RVI as Tutor in April 1946. For many years she was in-charge of the PTS. She became Principal Tutor on Miss Jackson's retirement and was appointed Principal Nursing Officer (Grade 9) Teaching Division in 1970. She retired in 1976 and died aged 86 years in 2002.

[5]   Patient's menus: when introduced into the RVI in 1966 they looked remarkably similar in design to the sample which Miss Shaw included in her report.

[6] Leazes Wing: The first patients were admitted in April 1972.

FLORENCE MAY OVINGTON MBE
Deputy Matron 1961 – 1970
Principal Nursing Officer 1970 – 1971
Divisional Nursing Officer (RVI/Central Group) 1971-1976

Florence May Ovington was born in Newcastle in January 1915, the first of two daughters born to Mathias and Lily; her father had been promoted from grocery assistant in his youth to grocery manager by 1939. The family lived in Kenton Lane, Gosforth for many years and this remained Miss Ovington's home until she moved into sheltered accommodation during her latter years.

Miss Ovington trained in the RVI 1934 -1937. In 1938 she undertook midwifery training at the Princess Mary Maternity Hospital. Subsequently she was employed for about a year as a private nurse by the Granville Nurses' Home[1] before moving on to the Sanderson Emergency Hospital in Gosforth, where she worked as both a staff nurse and ward sister between 1940 and 1945.

Matron Ovington

In April 1945 she took up a night sister's post at the Sunderland Royal Infirmary before becoming Home Sister in 1948, a post which she held for almost six years. In 1954 she was appointed to an Administrative Sister's post working along-side Miss Freda Shaw. Miss Ovington, described as "*a most efficient administrator*", remained at Sunderland Royal until her return to the RVI as Deputy Matron in July 1960. She held this position until 1970 when, as a consequence of the Salmon restructuring, she was appointed Principal Nursing Officer Grade 9. She was at this time still second-in-command under Miss Shaw; however, from 1971, with the formation of the Newcastle University Hospitals Group, she in effect became "Matron" of the Central Sector of which the Infirmary was the major institution.

In September 1972 Mr A J Carr replaced Miss Shaw as Chief Nursing Officer to the Newcastle University Hospitals Group. Further change followed with the move to a more integrated health service following the 1973 NHS Reorganisation Act.

The NHS Reorganisation Act 1973

This Act unified the separate functions of the hospital, family practitioner and community health services, all of which under the 1946 NHS Act were administered separately. With effect from the 1 April 1974 the 14 Regional Hospital Boards were replaced by Regional Health Authorities,[2] which delegated functions to the Area Health Authorities (AHAs). The latter were co-terminus with local authority boundaries to facilitate better cooperation *"to secure and advance the health and welfare of the people in England and Wales"*. Community Health Councils were established in each AHA to represent the interest of the patients and public in the health services. The Act also established the post of Health Services Commissioner to lead on the NHS complaints system.

Area Health Authorities now had responsibility for all the health services within the area: hospitals, school health services, health visitors, and domiciliary nursing and midwifery services; some, like Newcastle, with special responsibilities for medical and dental undergraduate teaching were designated AHAs (Teaching).

This reorganisation brought new opportunities for senior nurses as roles developed within the spheres of child health, service planning/capital works, personnel and in-service training.

Mr A J Carr became the Chief Nurse to the Newcastle Area Health Authority (Teaching) and Miss Ovington, still a Grade 9, became Divisional Nursing Officer (Central) with some modification to her area of control. As well as Castle Hill, the Babies Hospital, and the Dental Hospital, the regular dialysis unit based at Rye Hill Hospital and the Sanderson Orthopaedic Hospital all now came under the umbrella of the Central Division as did the Fleming Memorial Children's Hospital, and all those institutions[3] associated with it.

Following the restructuring instigated by the NHS Reorganisation Act, the rationalisation of nurse training had become inevitable and the three Schools of Nursing in the city amalgamated into the Newcastle Area School of Nursing[4]. The transition was managed by Newcastle AHA's new Director of Education, who was appointed in 1975 with overall responsibility for both pre- and post-basic nurse education.

The Area School of Nursing would from 1977, be based on the site of the newly commissioned Freeman Hospital[5]. The last intake of student nurses entering the RVI's School of Nursing was in 1976 - the year of Miss Ovington's retirement and soon after the retirement of the Principal Nurse Tutor, Miss Dixon. This brought to an end an era that had started in 1868 with the appointment of the Infirmary's probationers and from which the RVI School of Nursing would develop producing generations of nurses all proud of their heritage. On qualification this cohort of students was the last to receive the RVI's School of Nursing Badge

The Heath Awards, first presented to RVI nurses in 1906, had continued to be a feature of the life in the Infirmary up until this time, and in 1973 Dame Kathleen Raven[6], widow of Prof J T Ingram instituted an award in his name for a qualified nurse of outstanding service or ability.

Other aspects of life in the Infirmary which had changed included:
• Ancillary services had become subject to outside contracting, with the disappearance of many loyal and long-serving ward maids who had played such an important and valued part of the ward team.
• The introduction of the plated trolley service had brought an end to the traditional carving of the turkey on Christmas Day by the senior consultant on each ward.
• Another change was in respect to the nurses' Christmas dinner; this had for many years been served with the assistance of the junior medical staff whilst also engaging in some much appreciated entertainment. However by 1971 nurses were required to pay for their meals and Christmas dinner was no exception, with the old tradition disappearing from the calendar.
• That same year saw the demise of another much-loved feature of the Infirmary's Christmas season – the Christmas Concert, jointly produced by the nursing and junior medical staff, which gave them ample opportunity to cause much amusement at their seniors' expense! The staff canteen, which doubled-up as a concert hall, had now been up-graded into a self-service cafeteria and the concert hall facility was lost for ever.
• The separate dining-rooms for nurses and sisters were lost with all staff, excepting the senior medical staff who retained their consultants' dining room, now being able to eat in the dining room/canteen of their choice. The loss of the Sisters' Dining Room created a tremendous void in the informal peer-to-peer support which this facility had provided, especially for newly appointed Ward and Departmental Sisters.
• Another sign of the times was the loss of the tennis courts in the grounds of the Nurses' Home in 1972; the space was needed for the provision of extra changing rooms for the increasing numbers of non-resident nurses.
• In 1973 the National Uniform was introduced into the RVI with the students and pupils wearing white rather than the traditional grey and white stripes. Subsequently the staff nurses would exchange their grey uniforms for blue dresses and the ward sisters their mauve dresses[7] for navy blue.

Notable changes to the clinical services during these last years of Miss Ovington's time at the Infirmary was the opening, in 1973, of the Ursula Ridley Wing linked to Wards 8 & 16, which provided eight mother and baby rooms. This was followed in 1974 by the opening of the Regional Haemophilia Centre, and in 1975 by the delayed opening of the new and enlarged Accident & Emergency Department. The Babies Hospital, a much loved part of the Infirmary since 1948, was closed in 1976 when the Family Support Unit moved into the Fleming Memorial Hospital.

The pressures on the Ward and Departmental Sisters continued to escalate during this time. Ward sisters were now required to attend courses on management, art of examining and from 1974, staff appraisal. In addition, others were attending a day release City and Guilds Course leading to competence in Clinical Teaching. In 1972 a scheme was also introduced to establish closer links with the community services and the Ward Sisters were seconded in rotation to the community in Northumberland for one week.

The 1970s was also a time of industrial unrest that impacted on the Infirmary; the miners' strikes required strict economy in regard to heating and lighting; the ancillary workers' strike of 1973 caused considerable disruption, but nursing morale remained high with the levels of sick leave dropping significantly and the tremendous support of the Infirmary's senior nursing staff, the hospital secretary and the managers of the catering, laundry, and supplies departments were all greatly appreciated at ward level. The nurses' strike in 1974 caused minimal disruption, with most staff continuing to work normally; however they did welcome the outcome of the Halsbury Inquiry,[8] which resulted in considerable improvement in salaries! Table 36 summarises the 1974 pay increases.

Grade	Pre-Halsbury, 1970	Post-Halsbury, 1974
1st year Student Nurse	525	1125
3rd year Student Nurse	624	1325
Enrolled Nurse	801-969	1425-1902
Staff Nurse	930-1182	1692-2202
Ward Sister	1200-1554	2670-3300
Nursing Officer (Grade 7)	1572-1902	2775-3405
PNO/Divisional NO Grade10a)	2080-2435	5715-6435

Table 36. Nursing Salaries (£ p/a) before and after the 1974 Halsbury Pay Review

Miss Ovington took over the helm of the Infirmary's nursing service at a time of major transition. In addition to the massive advances in medical technology and the expansion of medical sub-specialties, which increased the demands for post-registration education and training; the role of ward sisters in respect of nurse training and staff development was becoming

166

more formalised and time consuming. The profession also had to cope with the implementation of the Salmon recommendations, which was quickly followed by the restructuring of services following the 1973 NHS Reorganisation. In the midst of all this change, the priority of responding to the nursing needs of the patients remained paramount. Miss Ovington deserved credit for maintaining the enthusiasm and morale of the Infirmary's nursing staff as the Infirmary transitioned from the old and familiar to the new and very much more unpredictable future. It was with great delight to the Infirmary's staff that Miss Ovington was awarded the MBE in New Years' Honours 1976, prior to her retirement in April of that year. She had served the Infirmary for 16 years as Deputy Matron and Matron and brought to an end an era of RVI nursing history.

Miss Ovington joined the Committee of the RVI Nurses' League in 1968 and became Chairman following Miss Shaw's retirement in July 1972. She continued to serve on the Committee until 1995 although she had stepped down from being Chairman in 1987, after which time she became Vice President

Miss Ovington at the 40th Anniversary of the Nurses' League in 1999

Miss Ovington with senior nurses in 1976

until her death. She died in Newcastle on 30 June 2006 on the evening a concert was held in the Sage to celebrate the 100th Anniversary of the transfer of services from the Royal Infirmary on the Forth Banks to the newly commissioned RVI on the Castle Leazes.

Timeline

1973   The United Kingdom joins the European Common Market

1974   Work on the new Dental Hospital and School commenced and opened in 1978

1976   The Royal College of Nursing registered as an independent trade union

---

[1] Granville Nurses' Home: This had originally been established in 1872 as the Nurses' Home and Training School, based in Charlotte Square.

[2] Dorothy Blenkinsop, RVI trained 1949-1953 and former Ward Sister to Ward 6, was appointed Regional Nursing Officer

[3] Institutions linked to the Fleming: The Nuffield Child Psychiatry Unit, Wellburn Nursery in Ovington, Ethel Watson Convalescent Home, Whitton Tower, Rothbury

[4] Newcastle Area School of Nursing: This was formed by the merger of those schools based in the RVI, Newcastle General Hospital and Walkergate Hospital.

[5] Freeman Hospital building was started in 1972 with the first patients being admitted in 1977. Subsequently in 1979 Joan Miller, recently SNO in the Infirmary, was appointed Divisional Nursing Officer. Miss Miller, trained in the RVI 1945-1949, and having been both a theatre sister and a surgical ward sister went on to pioneer the development of many new services in the Infirmary. Most notably, the anaesthetic department, the renal dialysis and transplant service and the intensive therapy unit.

[6] Dame Kathleen Raven was Chief Nursing Officer, Department of Health and Social Security 1957-1972. She married Prof J T Ingram, who came to Newcastle in 1959 as its first Professor of Dermatology; he died in 1972

[7] The Ward Sisters' mauve dresses: the tradition of this uniform coloured dress stemmed from the link with the Bishopric of Durham, the Lord Bishop of Durham having been the Grand Visitor to the Infirmary from the time of the founding of the Infirmary in 1751. The palatinate purple of the Bishop's robes has also been incorporated into the academic gowns of both Durham and Newcastle Universities.

[8] The Halsbury Inquiry into the pay of nurses and midwives and their conditions of service

Reflections

"Let whoever is in charge keep this simple question in her head: how can I provide for this right thing to be always done? To be 'in charge' is certainly not only to carry out the proper measures yourself but to see that everyone else does so too".
Florence Nightingale "Notes on Nursing"

My primary purpose has been to identify and record for posterity those individual Matrons who had served the Infirmary over a period of 225 years. The glimpses into the personal lives of these 22 ladies, who gave their best in a man's world with, up until now little recognition, have been fascinating. The research proved to be an absorbing journey through history.

Primarily it has been a journey through the history of nursing in the Infirmary as influenced by both local and national developments:

For over a century the day to day management of the Infirmary was in the hands of two resident officers, the Matron and initially the Apothecary, but from 1805 the Resident House Surgeon. The Matron was the Mistress of the 'House' with personal responsibility across the whole spectrum of house-hold management from recruitment to paying the wages, domestic services to laundry, catering to security, supplies officer to patient care. It was a position which required someone of reasonable social standing used to managing a household and servants. For the first 120 years the candidates of choice were widows and single women with experience in household or institution management.

It was the combination of the influence of Florence Nightingale along with the major developments in surgical practice that had followed the introduction of anaesthetic agents, and later by the adoption of antiseptic principles, which pushed the role of Matron to focus much more on the quality and skill of the nursing staff. In 1868, following Dr Charles John Gibb's survey of the nursing arrangements in sixteen hospitals in London and the provinces, some of the Matron's housekeeping responsibilities were delegated to a Housekeeper and the focus for the Matron, or Lady Superintendent of Nurses, shifted primarily to the supervision of nursing and nurses and with that to the training of probationers able to meet the increasing demands for skilled nurses in the Infirmary. The support of Dr George Yeoman Heath and Dr Frederick Page in this regard was mainly about improving the care of the patients in the

Infirmary, but also was about ensuring that there was a local pool of skilled nurses to provide care for their private patients nursed at home.

As the Infirmary broadened its purpose to provide training for probationer nurses so the need to provide accommodation, which safeguarded the moral welfare of suitable young ladies, placed new demands on the charity supporting the institution. Initially the 'Superintendents' of the Nurses' Homes were recruited for their credentials as suitable guardians in whom parents would have confidence in entrusting the welfare of their daughters. However, in time the Home Sister role was developed as a more specialised variation of the Assistant Matron, taking on specific responsibilities for the training of probationers. Once the General Nursing Council was established in 1920, nurse training was subjected to closer scrutiny at a national level and this was an incentive for the introduction of a Preliminary Training School and the appointment of the first nurse tutor in the early 1920's.

The First World War had left a surfeit of women many of whom were willing to dedicate their lives to their chosen vocation. However the demographic changes following the Second World War, along with the shift from local control to integration into a National Health Service, had a major impact on the staffing of hospitals. The Infirmary was no exception, as the reliance on resident, full-time, unmarried nurses shifted to an increasing dependence on non-resident, male, and part-time married nurses supported by enrolled nurses and nursing assistants. The need for improvements to the working conditions and salaries of nursing staff was now recognised nationally, and alongside this the Infirmary responded by introducing study blocks for nurses in training who were now designated as student nurses, rather than probationers.

Following the introduction of the NHS in 1948 there was a push for rationalisation and re-organisation of services as managers took over a range of ancillary services which had previously been within the remit of the Matron. By the 1970's Matrons were also losing control of the Schools of Nursing which were subject to merger not least in part response to the demand for post registration nurse training and education, reflecting the increasingly specialised nature of medical care. This process of rationalisation, reorganisation and restructuring continues to be a feature of today's NHS as it strives to balance the demand for services with the resources.

Some common themes however have transcended the passage of time and would be equally well recognised to some extent by all of the Infirmary's Matrons:
- Not enough beds, nurses or funds!
- Medical advances out-stripping available resources
- Inappropriate use of specialist services
- The pressure on beds resulting in the early discharge and lengthening

waiting lists
- Concerns about infection control
- Nurses assimilating into their practice those tasks formerly the province of the dressers, clerks and medical staff

Secondly it has been a journey through social history:

The Infirmary was initially built in a pleasant rural location, however over the following century it became swamped by the effects of industrialisation and population growth, before once again moving out into the parkland of the Leazes. With limited means of communication prior to the introduction of a postal system and telephones it was the local newspapers of the eighteenth and nineteen centuries which played a key role in reporting the business of the Infirmary. As we have seen the press was also the primary means of communicating with the subscribers and members of the Court of Governors not least in respect of the process of filling of vacancies for senior posts in the Infirmary. Even into the twentieth century, when access to telephones remained limited, the press was the only means by which many relatives were able to gain information regarding the condition of critically ill patients. Meanwhile the recurring problems of poverty, poor nutrition, and excessive alcohol consumption continue to impact on the health and well-being of many of today's patients just as they have done over the centuries.

Thirdly it has been a journey of surprises:

The first three Matrons all carried the surname Jackson, and there were unexpected family connections amongst some of the subsequent Matrons including a link with Eno of Fruit Salts fame. There are stories of orphans, a marriage, recovery from infectious disease, a suicide and a Matron who had worked in the docks. There have been Matrons who had travelled across continents and served far from the shores of home, sometimes in war zones. Some were involved either locally or nationally with the development of the territorial military nursing service whilst others were active in respect of nursing matters at a national level. At least two of the Matrons had been in correspondence with Florence Nightingale and it was a revelation to discover Mrs Ethel Bedford Fenwick's connection with Newcastle.

Finally the baton has been handed on:

In 2017 there were over 4100 nurses and midwives and almost 2000 health care assistants and other support staff employed across the hospitals in Newcastle. In addition to the traditional ward- and department-based nurses there are also a range of diverse roles for nurse specialists, practitioners and consultants. The title of 'Matron' was discarded in the 1970s but more recently has been reinvented as 'Modern Matron' charged with responsibility for discrete clinical specialties. It is noteworthy also that the Newcastle upon Tyne Hospitals NHS Foundation Trust, of which the RVI is part, currently has a nurse as its Chief Executive. In the year 2016/17 the Trust treated 203,584 inpatients and 1,083,654 outpatients; a far cry from the 167 and 178 respectively when the Infirmary opened in 1751. The original estimate for the annual budget of the Infirmary in 1751 was £530 and that of the Trust in 2017 was over £1billion.

Today's nurses however stand on the shoulders of those who have gone before and especially those pioneering Matrons who strived to improve standards of nursing care, firstly through the recruitment of 'suitable' probationers for whom they provided training and subsequently through a long campaign for registration. The great success of the NHS in providing patients with high quality and successful treatments would not have been possible without the leadership, dedication and sacrifice of those who have gone before. Whilst paying tribute to our predecessors, we must also look forward to the further development of health care, the blurring of professional boundaries and the continuing pivotal role to be played by nurses and their leaders.

APPENDIX 1

Voluntary Hospitals founded prior to the founding of the Newcastle Infirmary

By 1751 there were already fifteen other voluntary hospitals in England and Scotland, five in London and ten in the Provinces and Scotland

Those in London were founded as follows:

1720   Westminster Hospital
1724   Guy's Hospital
1733   St George's Hospital
1740   London Hospital
1745   Middlesex Hospital

These were in addition to St Bartholomew's and St Thomas's Hospitals both of which were originally religious establishments founded in the twelfth century, but re-founded as non-religious institutions following the dissolution of the monasteries.

Those in the Provinces & Scotland were founded as follows:

1729   Edinburgh Infirmary
1736   Winchester County Hospital
1737   Bristol Royal Infirmary
1740   York County Hospital
1741   Royal Devon and Exeter Hospital
1742   Bath General Hospital
1743   Northampton General Hospital
1746   Worcester Royal Infirmary
1747   Royal Salop Infirmary
1749   Liverpool Royal Infirmary

Manchester Infirmary and Leeds Infirmary came later in 1752 and 1767 respectively, and Glasgow Infirmary opened in 1794

APPENDIX 2

Ethel Bedford Fenwick (nee Manson) 1857-1947

Mrs Bedford Fenwick was the leader of the registration movement. She had trained as a lady probationer at the Children's Hospital Nottingham before spending a further year at Manchester Royal Infirmary. Following time as a sister at the London Hospital, in 1881 at the age of 24 she was appointed Matron of St Bartholomew's Hospital. She resigned this post 1887 when she married Dr Eric Bedford Fenwick who was born in North Shields and graduated in 1877 from Durham University. His father practised medicine in North Shields.

She was the founder of the British Nurses' Association in 1887 - subsequently the Royal British Nurses' Association (RBNA). Between 1906 and 1909 the RBNA drafted three parliamentary bills on nurse registration. In 1917 there were inconclusive discussions on the possibility of a merger between the RBNA and the College of Nursing, which had been established the previous year.

In 1888 she founded the International Council of Nurses, becoming its first President. In 1893 she and her husband acquired the journal the 'Nursing Record', first published in 1888, and she became its Editior. It was renamed the 'British Journal of Nursing' in 1902.

Together with Isla Stewart she founded the Matron's Council of Great Britain and Ireland in 1894, and in 1902 she became the secretary and treasurer of the newly formed Society for the State Registration of Nurses. In 1904 these two organisations merged to form the National Council of Trained Nurses of Great Britain and Ireland with Mrs Bedford Fenwick becoming its first president.

The Central Committee for the State Registration of Nurses was formed in 1909 with Mrs Ethel Bedford Fenwick becoming joint honorary secretary. Between 1910 and 1914 the Central Committee introduced annual Parliamentary bills on nurse registration.

The General Nursing Council (GNC) chaired by Mrs Bedford Fenwick was established following the 1919 Nurses' Registration Act and she in turn became No 1 on the Register. She lost her seat on the GNC following the elections held in 1922. In 1926 she founded the British College of Nursing with herself as President and her husband as Treasurer; it closed in 1956 nine years after her death in 1947.

POSTSCRIPT - The Newcastle Connection: The Bedford Fenwick's had one son Christian Bedford Fenwick who was educated at Eton and Magdalen College Oxford. He was a barrister at law and King's Counsel. He married Mary Beatrice Wait in Jesmond Parish Church in 1915. The couple lived in Lambton Road, Jesmond for many years and had two sons: Arthur who died in a road traffic accident in 1955 and David Belasyse Bedford Fenwick who died in 2012 and is buried in Jesmond Old Cemetery. Christian died in Newcastle in 1988. Mary Beatrice was on the negotiating committee of the Fleming Memorial Hospital in 1939 following a decision to amalgamate that hospital with both the Children's Department of the RVI and the Babies Hospital on the Castle Leazes site. She was also Chairman of the Ladies Committee of the Princess Mary Maternity Hospital. She died in 1953.

APPENDIX 3

Changes in the "authorities" responsible for the governance of the Infirmary from 1971 and the associated Chief Nurses/Directors of Nursing

The Governing Bodies

From 1971	Newcastle University Hospitals Group, RVI being one of three Divisions (Central)
From 1974	Newcastle Area Health Authority (Teaching)
From 1982	Newcastle Health Authority
From 1992	RVI & Associated Hospitals NHS Trust
From 1998	Newcastle upon Tyne Hospitals NHS Trust
From 2004	Newcastle upon Tyne Hospitals NHS Foundation Trust

The 'Chief Nurses' of the Newcastle Hospitals 1971 -2019

Chief Nursing Officers:
Miss Freda Shaw	1971 - 1972

Chief Nursing Officer/Area Nursing Officer
Mr Anthony Carr	1972 - 1982

Chief Nursing Officer
Mr William Boland	1982 - 1992

Director of Patient Services
Mrs Lyn Simpson	1998 - 2004

Director of Nursing & Patient Services
Mrs Lyn Simpson	2004 - 2005
Mrs Melanie Hornett	2005 - 2009
Mrs Helen Lamont	2009 - 2018
Ms Maurya Cushlow	2018 - present

The 'Matrons' of the Infirmary from 1971 -2019

Divisional Nursing Officer

Miss F M Ovington	1971 - 1976
Mrs Jean Turner	1976 - 1982

Director of Nursing Services Central

Mr Brian Footit	1983 - 1986

Head of Nursing/Director of Nursing

Miss E Anne Nicholson	1986 - 1992

Executive Director of Nursing (RVI & Associated Hospitals NHS Trust)

Miss E Anne Nicholson (later Craft)	1992 - 1994
Miss B Pat Kelly	1994 - 1998

Head of Nursing

Mr Chris Piercy	1998 - 2002

Deputy Director of Nursing & Patient Services

Mrs Helen Lamont	2002 - 2009
Mrs Elizabeth Harris	2009 - 2018

Deputy Chief Nurse

Mrs Elizabeth Harris	2018 - present

APPENDIX 4

Provision in Newcastle for the Training & Education of Nurses from 1976

1976 Newcastle University Hospitals Group School of Nursing
Newcastle Area School of Nursing

1991 Newcastle and Northumbria College of Nursing and Midwifery, incorporating:
> Newcastle Area School,
> Newcastle & Northumbria College of Midwifery and
> Northumberland School of Nursing

1993 Bede, Newcastle and Northumbria College of Nursing and Midwifery

1995 Faculty of Health, Education and Social Sciences in the University of Northumbria at Newcastle

Principal Sources Consulted

Infirmary Archives

Annual Reports of the Infirmary
House Committee Minutes
Honorary Staff Committee Minutes
Nursing Committee Minutes

On-line genealogy sources

Births Marriages and Death
Census
Nursing Registers
Probate records
The British Newspaper Archive

Other on-line sources

Kings College London: Collection of Pioneering Nurses
RCN Historical Nursing Journals
Butler, Graham A, Diseases, Medicine & the Urban Poor in
Newcastle upon Tyne 1750-1850, (Unpublished PhD Thesis:
Newcastle University 2012)

Bibliography

Baly, Monica, 1997 Florence Nightingale and the Nursing Legacy, Whurr
Publishers, London

Baly, Monica, 1980 Nursing and Social Change, 2nd edition Heineman
Medical Books Ltd, London

Hume, G H, 1906 History of the Newcastle Infirmary, Andrew Reid & Co
Ltd

Hume, W E, 1951The Infirmary Newcastle upon Tyne 1751-1951 A Brief
Sketch, Andrew Reid & Co Ltd

McDonald, Lynn, 2009 (Editor) Florence Nightingale: Extending Nursing,
Wilfred Laurier University-UTP

Walton, J & Irving, M, 2006, 100 years of the 1906-2006, RVI , Newcastle
upon Tyne Hospitals NHS Trust

Turner, G & Arnison, W D, 1934 The Newcastle upon Tyne School of
Medicine 1834-1934, Andrew Reid & Co Ltd

Wake, Roy 1998 The Nightingale Training School 1860-1996, Haggerston
Press

Acknowledgements

My research into the Matrons of the Infirmary began several years ago as a matter of personal interest, but once the decision was made to publish I have received tremendous support from numerous people and organisations to whom I am indebted.

Special thanks must go to my husband Alan for his unstinting support, wise counsel, and patience, and also to my grandchildren Martha and William for their understanding over recent months as to why I have not always been as attentive to them as I would have liked. I would also like to thank Xenia Webster, Jill and Mike Reid for their help.

I am indebted to both Newcastle Hospitals NHS Trust and the Tyne & Wear Archives for giving me access to archival material and photographs, as well as to the Robinson Library Newcastle University, and the London Metropolitan Archives. I am most grateful to the Royal College of Nursing Archives for allowing me to use photographs of Matron's MacKey and McCall Anderson.

Thanks also go to those members of the RVI Nurses' League who have responded with goodwill to my requests for information and photographs. I am especially grateful to Ann Clouston, Maureen Fearns, and Helen Lamont for previewing some of the text as well as to Catherine Atkinson, and her husband Peter for the photographs of the 1902 Coronation Cuthbert Cross.

Finally I must thank David Hepworth and Derek Tree at Tyne Bridge Publishing for their advice and guidance in finalising this book.